THE LIFE OF CHRIST IN CROSSWORD PUZZLES

THE LIFE OF CHRIST IN CROSSWORD PUZZLES

Containing 52 puzzles based on incidents from the life and teachings of Christ. Taken from Matthew, Mark, Luke and John

BY

LUCILE PETTIGREW JOHNSON

BAKER BOOK HOUSE
Grand Rapids, Michigan

Standard Book Number: 8010-5000-6

THE LIFE OF CHRIST IN CROSSWORD PUZZLES

PHOTOLITHOPRINTED BY CUSHING - MALLOY, INC.
ANN ARBOR, MICHIGAN, UNITED STATES OF AMERICA
1970

In loving memory of my mother

Lucy Ervin Pettigrew

whose noble Christian life was
a help and inspiration
to many.

FOREWORD

"They are they which testify of me."—John 5:39

When Christ uttered these words, he was speaking of the Scriptures. Since that day, there have been countless other writings that have testified of his life and love. Stories have been told, based on the Scriptures, telling of his goodness and mercy; articles have been written of his deeds, his power, and his kindness; songs have been sung of his holiness and glory; and now, the cross-word puzzles, too, in their way, are testifying of his character and teachings.

The puzzles in this book are based upon the life of Christ. Of course, in a work of this size, a selection of incidents must be made; it would be impossible to include them all. There are many Bible passages quoted in which the word to be found is designated by three dots. The majority of these quotations are from the four Gospels, although some are found in other parts of the Bible. Names of people and places mentioned in the Bible are also to be found in the missing words.

We hope that those who solve these puzzles will find them interesting, entertaining, and helpful.

NUMBER 1

THE BIRTH OF JESUS

HORIZONTAL

1 "That at the name of . . . every knee should bow" Phil. 2:10
5 The . . . of the 13 across
10 Snakelike fish
11 "Ye are my friends, if ye . . . whatsoever I command you" John 15:14
13 The . . . was full
14 "And, . . . , the angel of the Lord came upon them" Luke 2:9
15 Small bird
17 "there . . . out a decree from Caesar Augustus" Luke 2:1
18 A town of Benjamin I Chron. 8:12
19 Joseph . . . from his dream
20 Son of Jahdai, of the family of Caleb I Chron. 2:47
23 Of
25 Second note of scale
26 Territory in Palestine
29 "Behold the . . . of God" John 1:29
32 Native mineral
33 "Let there be . . . strife" Gen. 13:8
35 Mary was the . . . of Joseph
36 "and laid him in a . . . " Luke 2:7
38 Same as 18 down
39 Self
41 "all went to be . . . " Luke 2:3
43 Indian moccasins
45 "The trees of the Lord are full of . . . " Ps. 104:16
46 "with all thy heart, and with all thy . . . " Matt. 22:37
47 "in the days of . . . the king" Matt. 2:1
49 "And it came to . . . in those days" Luke 2:1
51 "Go out quickly into the streets and . . . of the city" Luke 14:21
53 Hebrew deity
54 Plural ending of nouns
56 Kiln
57 Silent

VERTICAL

1 "born King of the . . . " Matt. 2:2
2 Ever (cont.)
3 Herod . . . the children
4 South Dakota
5 "When Herod the . . . had heard these things" Matt. 2:3
6 " . . . thou into the joy of thy lord" Matt. 25:21
7 Half an em
8 Father of two of David's guards I Chron. 11:46
9 "there was no . . . for them in the inn" Luke 2:7
12 "which . . . him ten thousand talents" Matt. 18:24
16 "there is . . . good but one, that is God" Matt. 19:17
18 Exclamation
21 Without regard to self
22 Man who helped Aaron hold up Moses' hands at battle with Amalek Ex. 17:12
24 Ancestor of Jesus Luke 3:28
26 Earthly father of Jesus
27 Adherent of democracy
28 Prophetess who saw Jesus Luke 2:36
30 Diphthong
31 " . . . , I bring you good tidings" Luke 2:10
34 King of Bashan Num. 32:33
35 " . . . him in swaddling clothes" Luke 2:7
37 Greek letter
40 Celts
42 Administers medicine
44 Jesus was the . . . of God
48 "in the morning the . . . lay round about the host" Ex. 16:13
50 " . . . we like sheep have gone astray" Isa. 53:6
52 "Let your light . . . shine" Matt. 5:16
55 Sunday School

"Thou shalt call his name JESUS: for he shall save his people from their sins." — Matt. 1:21

NUMBER 2

THE VISIT OF THE MAGI

HORIZONTAL

1 "with exceeding great . . . " Matt. 2:10
3 "they saw the . . . " Matt. 2:10
6 Age
9 City in the northeast of Canaan Num. 34:11
10 Mohammedan chief
13 "lying . . . a manger" Luke 2:12
14 and 15 "The Magi were the . . . . . . "
17 Herod . . . the wise men to 23 down
19 They brought . . .
21 "out of thee shall come . . . Governor" Matt. 2:6
22 No good
23 "demanded of them where Christ should . . . born" Matt. 2:4
24 Golf mound
25 Evergreen tree
26 "called the altar . . . " Josh. 22:34
28 "they departed into their own country another . . . " Matt. 2:12
31 "they forsook their . . . , and followed him" Mark 1:18
32 Simeon took Jesus in his . . . , and blessed God
34 Jesus was named when he was eight days . . .
35 Beverage
36 Anger
37 A gift of the Magi
39 "Ye . . . my friends, if ye do whatsoever I command you" John 15:14
41 They came to . . . Jesus
43 Native mineral
44 Another gift of the Magi
46 Destitute of thorns
50 "there is . . . God" Mark 12:32
51 "they had . . . their treasures" Matt. 2:11

VERTICAL

2 "Bethlehem . . . Judaea"
3 "And they . . . unto him" Matt. 2:5
4 "purge away thy dross, and take away all thy . . . " Isa. 1:25
5 "hath raised up . . . horn of salvation for us" Luke 1:69
6 "we have seen his star in the . . . " Matt. 2:2
7 Poem
8 Symbol for nickel
10 Herod was . . . of Judaea
11 Servant of Solomon Ezra 2:57
12 Comes in
14 "the star, which they saw in the east, . . . before them" Matt. 2:9
16 Small lizard
18 Race from which Jesus was descended
19 "be called . . . in the kingdom of heaven" Matt. 5:19
20 Southeast
23 Place of Christ's birth
25 "When . . . have found him, bring me word again" Matt. 2:8
27 "being warned of God in a . . . that they should not return to Herod" Matt. 2:12
28 They fell down to . . . him
29 On the lee side
30 Yard
33 Mother of Jesus
37 " . . . and search diligently" Matt. 2:8
38 "Do men gather grapes of thorns, . . . figs of thistles" Matt. 7:16
40 "come down . . . my child die" John 4:49
42 Paradise
45 " . . . , I am with you alway" Matt. 28:20
47 Northeast
48 Second note in scale
49 Maryland

"They presented unto him gifts; gold, and frankincense, and myrrh." — Matt. 2:11.

NUMBER 3

THE SHEPHERDS

HORIZONTAL

2 "flowers appear . . . the earth" S. of S. 2:12
4 "Son of man hath power on . . . to forgive sins" Matt. 9:6
8 "Lord God of . . . was with him" 2 Sam. 5:10
11 Lava
12 "which shall . . . to all people" Luke 2:10
13 Hebrew deity
14 "they were sore . . . " Luke 2:9
18 Second note of scale
19 Household animals
21 Plural of suffix denoting person or agent
22 To tear
23 City of Benjamin Gen. 12:8
24 "am come to send . . . on earth" Matt. 10:34
25 Tropical American cuckoo
26 "He hath not . . . with us after our sins" Ps. 103:10
27 "And this shall be a . . . unto you" Luke 2:12
28 A friend of David I Kings 1:8
30 Heritable land
32 Son of Jacob
33 "suddenly there was with the . . . a multitude of the heavenly host" Luke 2:13
36 "know how to give . . . gifts" Matt. 7:11
39 "not my . . . , but thine, be done" Luke 22:42
40 " . . . , and it shall be given you" Matt. 7:7
41 Indian plant
43 "Let us now . . . even unto Bethlehem" Luke 2:15
44 Fifth month of Hebrew year
46 North Carolina
47 "For the Son of man is come to seek and to . . . that which is lost" Luke 19:10
49 Part of the day
50 "And, . . . , the angel of the Lord came upon them" Luke 2:9
51 Gold (Heraldry; pl.)
53 Fourscore
55 " . . . if he ask a fish, will he give him a serpent" Matt. 7:10
56 "eyes are ever . . . the Lord" Ps. 25:15
57 Plural noun ending
58 "Oh that . . . would praise the Lord" Ps. 107:8
Saying of the angels is 2, 4, 24, 36, 39, 56, and 58 combined

VERTICAL

1 "And the . . . returned, glorifying and praising God" Luke 2:20
2 Bone
3 New Testament
5 "to . . . up children unto Abraham" Luke 3:8
6 Tot
7 " . . . watch over their flock by night" Luke 2:8
9 Trees of olive family
10 South America
12 "I . . . you good tidings" Luke 2:10
15 "abiding in the . . . " Luke 2:8
16 Lariat (Sp.)
17 Part of a circle
20 The angel brought good . . .
22 Instrument for evening yarn on loom (Scot.)
24 Old Italian coin
29 Each
31 "written in the . . . of the Lord" Luke 2:23
34 "rain was upon the earth forty days and forty . . . " Gen. 7:12
35 " . . . to God in the highest" Luke 2:14
37 Indorsements
38 King of Judah and Israel
40 Topmost, a combining form
42 "greaves of brass upon his . . .s" I Sam. 17:6
44 "brought a mixture of myrrh and . . .s" John 19:39
45 "unto you is . . . this day in the city of David, a Saviour" Luke 2:11
46 "the angel said unto them, Fear . . . " Luke 2:10
48 Relation to air, a combining form
52 Southwest
54 " . . . that is not with me is against me" Matt. 12:30

1	■	2	3	■	■	4		5	6		■	7
8	9			10	■	■	■	11		■	12	
13		■	■	14	15	16	17			■	18	
19		20		■	21				■	22		
23			■	24					■	25		
	■	26					■	■	27			
28	29		■	30			31	■	■		■	
32			■		■	■	33	34	35			■
	■	36	37		38	■	39				■	■
■	40			■	41	42	■	43		■	44	45
46		■	47	48			■	49		■	50	
51		52	■	53			54			■	55	
56						■	57		■	58		

"And there were in the same country shepherds abiding in the field." — Luke 2:8.

NUMBER 4

THE PRESENTATION

HORIZONTAL

1 To and upon
4 "A . . . to lighten the Gentiles" Luke 2:32
9 " . . . I was an hungred, and ye gave me meat" Matt. 25:35
10 "heareth these sayings of . . . , and doeth them" Matt. 7:24
11 "lord, that our . . . may be opened" Matt. 20:33
13 Sacred East Indian tree
15 Born
17 Symbol for tellurium
18 Jesus was brought to the temple by his . . .
19 Greek letter
20 Second note
21 "according to the . . . of Moses" Luke 2:22
22 "and the glory of thy people . . . " Luke 2:32
23 City in France
25 . . . Luke
26 "For if ye love them which love you, what reward . . . ye" Matt. 5:46
29 "not see death, before he had . . . the Lord's Christ" Luke 2:26
30 "a sword shall pierce through . . . own soul also" Luke 2:35
32 Compass point
33 "and for a sign which shall . . . spoken against" Luke 2:34
34 Soil Conservation Service
36 "ye pay tithe of mint and . . . and cummin" Matt. 23:23
38 Jesus received his name when he was . . . days old
40 Large covered wagon
41 The . . . of the Apostles
44 "they returned into . . . " Luke 2:39
48 "And all flesh shall see the . . . of God" Luke 3:6
50 Molded curd of milk
51 "which was . . . named of the angel" Luke 2:21
A saying of Simeon is 9, 10, 11, 26, 29, 30, and 48 combined

VERTICAL

1 "to . . . a sacrifice" Luke 2:24
2 "I have not found so great faith, . . . , not in Israel" Luke 7:9
3 "they set a . . . , they catch men" Jer. 5:26
4 "gave thanks . . . unto the Lord" Luke 2:38
5 "this child is set for the fall and rising again of many . . . Israel" Luke 2:34
6 "For after all these things do the . . . seek" Matt. 6:32
7 Golf mound
8 "but . . . it on a candlestick" Luke 8:16
10 Spiritual
12 "the . . . of mine apostleship are ye in the Lord" I Cor. 9:2
14 Salt
16 Spiritual being
19 "many shall come from the . . . and west" Matt. 8:11
24 Southeast
26 "the . . . were opened unto him" Matt. 3:16
27 Prophetess who saw Christ in the temple
28 "there is a . . . for the silver" Job 28:1
31 "Do not ye . . . understand" Matt. 15:17
33 Small hound
35 . . . took Jesus in his arms
37 Book of maps
39 "And . . . came by the Spirit into the temple" Luke 2:27
42 "It was a . . . , and a stone lay upon it" John 11:38
43 Location
45 Chinese measure
46 Half an em
47 "A pair of turtledoves or . . . young pigeons" Luke 2:24
48 South Carolina
49 "Then said I, . . . , Lord God! behold I cannot speak" Jer. 1:6

1	2	3		■	4	5	6		7	■	8	■
9			■	10				■	11			12
	■	13	14			■	15	16		■	17	
	■	18							■	19		
20		■	21			■	22					
■	■	■	■	23		24			■	25		■
26	27	28		■	29				■	30		31
32			■	33		■	34		35	■	■	
36					■	37	■	38			39	
40			■	41	42		43	■		■		■
	■	■	■	44				45		46	■	47
	■	48	49								■	
	■	50						■		■	51	

"They brought him to Jerusalem, to present him to the Lord." — Luke 2:22.

NUMBER 5

THE VISIT OF THE BOY JESUS TO THE TEMPLE

HORIZONTAL

2 "Joseph . . . his mother knew not of it" Luke 2:43
4 "the child . . . tarried behind" Luke 2:43
9 " . . . , I am with you alway" Matt. 28:20
10 German
11 "Suffer it to be . . . now" Matt. 3:15
12 "and . . . in number daily" Acts 16:5
15 Man's nickname
16 Southeast
17 "I am like an . . . of the desert" Ps. 102:6
18 "his mother kept all these sayings . . . her heart" Luke 2:51
20 "filled with . . . " Luke 2:40
23 Doctor of Philosophy
25 "after the custom . . . the feast" Luke 2:42
26 Northeast
27 "Why callest thou . . . good" Luke 18:19
28 "thy father . . . I have sought thee" Luke 2:48
29 "can add to his . . . one cubit" Luke 12:25
32 Tin
33 Court
35 "both hearing them, . . . asking them questions" Luke 2:46
37 "supposing him to have been . . . the company" Luke 2:44
38 "thou hast found . . . with God" Luke 1:30
40 "twelve . . . old" Luke 2:42
42 Sun god
43 Member of the Numismatical Society
44 "And he went down . . . them" Luke 2:51
46 "the grace of . . . was upon him" Luke 2:40
49 Didymium
50 "Joshua, the son of . . . " Ex. 33:11
52 "Then said I, . . . , Lord God" Jer. 1:6
53 To mature
54 Grand Secretary
55 " . . . when they found him not" Luke 2:45
56 "How much then is a . . . better than a sheep" Matt. 12:12
57 Second note in scale
Our text about the Boy Jesus is 2, 4, 12, 18, 20, 28, 29, 35, 37, 38, 44, 46, 55, and 56 combined

VERTICAL

1 "when they saw him, they were . . . " Luke 2:48
2 Elsewhere
3 Not
4 Gee
5 Age
6 "pray for them which despitefully . . . you" Luke 6:28
7 "more tolerable in that day for . . . " Luke 10:12
8 "when he was . . . years old" Luke 2:42
10 "And the child . . . " Luke 2:40
13 Civil Service
14 "And he was . . . at that saying" Mark 10:22
19 Bow
21 "Jesus entered . . . Jerusalem" Mark 11:11
22 . . . of Galilee
24 Plush
27 Same as 27 across
29 "said unto him, . . . , why hast thou" Luke 2:48
30 Beverage
31 "there was no . . . for them in the inn" Luke 2:7
32 "understood not the . . . which he spake" Luke 2:50
33 " . . . ye not that I must be about" Luke 2:49
34 Resembling a bear
36 "began to . . . toward the first day of the week" Matt. 28:1
38 Exhaust
39 "when thou wast . . . the fig tree" John 1:48
41 Japanese measure
45 "when they . . . fulfilled the days" Luke 2:43
47 Anglo-Saxon money
48 Noise
51 "thus dealt with . . . " Luke 2:48

1	■	2	3		■	4	5		6	7	■	8
	■	9		■	10			■	11		■	
	■	12		13				14			■	
15			■	16		■	■		■	17		
	■	18	19	■	20	21	22				■	
23	24	■	25		■	26		■	■	■	27	
■	28			■	29			30		31		■
32		■	■	33			■		■		■	34
35		36	■	37		■	38				39	
40			41		■	42		■	■	43		
	■	44			45	■	46	47	48	■	49	
50	51		■	■	52		■	53				
54		■	55			■	56			■	57	

"And all that heard him were astonished at his understanding and answers." — Luke 2:47.

NUMBER 6

JOHN THE BAPTIST

HORIZONTAL

1 "Behold, I send my . . . before thy face" Mark 1:2
9 Worthy Patriarch
11 "Come ye yourselves apart into a desert place, and . . . a while" Mark 6:31
12 " . . . up children unto Abraham" Luke 3:8
13 " . . . is my flesh of brass" Job 6:12
14 Lava
15 Ruthenium
17 " . . . ye the way of the Lord" Luke 3:4
19 "As . . . is written in the prophets" Mark 1:2
20 "ye shall find an . . . tied" Matt. 21:2
22 Scandinavian book
23 "strike the . . . and the two side posts with the blood" Ex. 12:22
25 North America
26 And (F.)
28 Cavity of hollow rock nodule
29 Transpose
30 "I find . . . fault in this man" Luke 23:4
31 "the kingdom of heaven is at . . . " Matt. 3:2
32 Seventh note in scale
33 "We have walked . . . and fro through the earth" Zech. 1:11
34 "But if thine . . . be evil" Matt. 6:23
36 "girdle of a . . . " Mark 1:6
39 "On these two commandments . . . all the law and the prophets" Matt. 22:40
40 "camel's . . . " Matt. 3:4
43 Indorsements
44 Pertaining to an ellipse
49 Each
51 "preaching in the . . . of Judaea" Matt. 3:1
53 Railroad
54 New Mexico
55 "with silver, iron, . . . , and lead" Ezek. 27:12
56 "how can we know the . . . " John 14:5

VERTICAL

1 "his . . . was locusts and wild honey" Matt. 3:4
2 Plural ending of nouns
3 "make his paths . . . " Matt. 3:3
4 Ancestor of Jesus Luke 3:28
5 A little sleep
6 "and a leathern . . . about his loins" Matt. 3:4
7 Compass point
8 "And saying, . . . ye" Matt. 3:2
9 "the . . . of God came unto John" Luke 3:2
10 " . . . the baptism of repentance" Luke 3:3
11 "had his . . . of camel's hair" Matt. 3:4
16 Genus of lichens
18 Twelfth month of Jewish year
21 "God is able of these . . . to raise up children" Matt. 3:9
24 Circular whirl of air or water
27 Also
32 "confessing their . . . " Mark 1:5
35 Hebrew deity
36 "the latchet of whose . . . I am not worthy to unloose" Luke 3:16
37 New Zealand parrot
38 "every mountain and . . . shall be brought low" Luke 3:5
40 "every tree which bringeth not forth good fruit is . . . down" Matt. 3:10
41 Mohammedan religious teacher
42 "and I will . . . evil beasts out of the land" Lev. 26:6
45 Household animal
46 Three
47 "no room for them in the . . . " Luke 2:7
48 Civil Engineer
50 "The voice of one . . .ing in the wilderness" Matt. 3:3
52 "if God . . . clothe the grass" Matt. 6:30
53 Sun god

	1	2	3		4	5	6	7	8		9	10
11					12						13	
14			15	16		17				18		
19			20		21				22			
		23				24			25			
26	27		28						29			
30			31								32	
33					34		35		36	37		
		38							39			
40	41		42						43			
44				45	46	47	48		49			50
51								52			53	
54				55						56		

"Repent ye: for the kingdom of heaven is at hand." — Matt. 3:2.

NUMBER 7

THE BAPTISM OF JESUS

HORIZONTAL

1 " . . . was he of whom I spake" John 1:15
2 "who coming after me . . . preferred before me" John 1:27
4 "I and . . . Father are one" John 10:30
6 Sunday School
9 Levite sent by Jehoshaphat to teach people in Judah II Chron. 17:8
12 " . . . it to be so now" Matt. 3:15
17 "descending like a . . . " Matt. 3:16
18 Gate of the temple in Jerusalem II Kings 11:6
19 "touched the . . . of his garment" Matt. 9:20
21 "when he saw . . . , he said, Daughter, be of" Matt. 9:22
22 and 23 "Thou art my . . . . . . " Luke 3:22
25 Field Marshal
26 Adjust
28 Ezra
29 Greek letter
32 Tropical American cuckoo
33 Color
34 Thin slabs of baked clay
36 "every good . . . bringeth forth good fruit" Matt. 7:17
37 "Whose fan is . . . his hand" Matt. 3:12
38 "this is he, of . . . it is written" Matt. 11:10
40 and 41 " . . . . . . God, even thy God" Ps. 50:7
43 "whether he . . . the Christ, or not" Luke 3:15
44 And
45 Large covered wagon
47 Plural ending of nouns
49 Seventh note in scale
50 Chapter in Matt. and Luke that tells of the temptation of Jesus
51 Downright
52 "unto you is born this . . . in the city of David" Luke 2:11
54 Third note
55 Girl's name
56 and 57 "in thee I am . . . . . . " Luke 3:22

Saying of the voice from heaven is 1, 2, 4, 22, 23, 38, 40, 41, 56, and 57 combined

VERTICAL

1 It is (cont.)
3 Saint
4 Bachelor of Music
5 A Jew (Colloq.)
6 "to . . . life, or to kill" Mark 3:4
7 Messenger mentioned in Zech. 7:2
8 "and comest thou to . . . " Matt. 3:14
10 Unit of electrical resistance
11 "But . . . forbad him, saying" Matt. 3:14
13 "When ye pray, . . . not vain repetitions" Matt. 6:7
14 "thus it becometh us to . . . all righteousness" Matt. 3:15
15 "And lo a voice . . . heaven" Matt. 3:17
16 Fifth satellite of Saturn
20 Book of Scandinavian mythology
22 "unto John, to be . . . of him" Matt. 3:13
23 "and the . . . like a dove descending upon him" Mark 1:10
24 Old Testament
27 "Go to the . . . , thou sluggard" Prov. 6:6
28 Evangelical Union
30 "which taketh away the . . . of the world" John 1:29
31 Son of Manasseh I Chron. 7:14
33 "and, lo, the . . . were opened unto him" Matt. 3:16
35 "two hundred . . . , and twenty rams" Gen. 32:14
39 Whirlwind off the Faroe Islands
42 River in France
44 "but deliver us from . . . " Matt. 6:13
46 "I have . . . to be baptized of thee" Matt. 3:14
48 "and he . . . the Spirit of God descending" Matt. 3:16
50 Mischievous child
51 A bird, the mew (Scot.); calf's call
53 " . . . are they which justify yourselves" Luke 16:15

1					2	3		4	5		6	7
				8		9	10			11		
12	13	14	15		16				17			
	18				19	20				21		
22								23	24			
		25			26		27				28	
29	30			31		32				33		
34			35				36					
37			38		39			40		41	42	
		43					44			45		46
47	48		49			50			51			
52		53				54			55			
	56					57						

"Then cometh Jesus from Galilee to Jordan unto John, to be baptized of him." — Matt. 3:13.

NUMBER 8

THE THREE TEMPTATIONS OF JESUS

HORIZONTAL

1 "led by the Spirit into the . . . " Luke 4:1
10 "neither in this mountain, nor yet . . . Jerusalem" John 4:21
12 Dolphin
13 "Get thee behind me, . . . " Luke 4:8
14 "for that is delivered unto . . . " Luke 4:6
15 Lock of hair
16 City of Benjamin east of Bethel Gen. 12:8
17 Two books of the Old Testament
18 "taking him up into an . . . mountain" Luke 4:5
19 To let the bait fall lightly on the water
21 "Then was Jesus . . . up" Matt. 4:1
24 "If thou be the Son of God, . . . thyself down" Matt. 4:6
27 "He . . . give his angels charge over thee" Luke 4:10
29 . . . Homo
30 "when he had . . . forty days and forty nights" Matt. 4:2
32 "man shall not live by . . . alone" Luke 4:4
33 Province in Canada
35 "set him . . . a pinnacle" Luke 4:9
36 National Recovery Administration
37 Crown of India
40 Looks after
41 Takes off
43 Destruction
45 City of the Ammonites, near Heshbon Jer. 49:3
46 A Shilonite, dwelling in Jerusalem I Chron. 9:5
48 "all the kingdoms of the . . . " Luke 4:5
50 "there . . . none good but one" Mark 10:18
51 "setteth him on a . . . of the temple" Matt. 4:5

VERTICAL

1 "and was . . . the wild beasts" Mark 1:13
2 Inscription; Jesus of Nazareth, King of the Jews
3 Sovereign
4 "thou . . . thy foot against a stone" Luke 4:11
5 Recording Secretary
6 Nahum
7 Greek letter
8 "And Jesus answered and . . . unto him" Luke 4:8
9 Tin
10 Wine vessel of the early Christian church
11 "to be . . . of the devil" Matt. 4:1
17 "about the . . . of one hour" Luke 22:59
20 Generic name of the maple
21 Dialect of southeastern Switzerland
22 Hebrew deity
23 Deputy Lieutenant
25 Disfigure
26 "Whence hath this . . . this wisdom" Matt. 13:54
27 "house divided against itself shall not . . . " Matt. 12:25
28 "Jesus saith unto . . . , Woman, believe me" John 4:21
30 "Being . . . days tempted of the devil" Luke 4:2
31 "command that these . . . be made bread" Matt. 4:3
34 Conjunction
37 Beverage
38 " . . . thou be the Son of God" Matt. 4:3
39 "And he took him . . . from the multitude" Mark 7:33
41 "cast thyself . . . from hence" Luke 4:9
42 "if thou wilt . . . down and worship me" 4:9
43 "her . . . was to light on a part of the field belonging unto Boaz" Ruth 2:3
44 An Israelite of the tribe of Asher I Chron. 7:34
46 "looking upon Jesus . . . he walked" John 1:36
47 "the latchet of whose shoes I . . . not worthy to unloose" Luke 3:16
49 Reformed Church

1	2	3	4		5	6	7	8	9		10	11
12					13						14	
15						16				17		
18								19	20			
					21	22	23		24		25	
	26		27	28					29			
30		31						32				
33						34						
		35			36				37	38		39
40								41			42	
					43	44					45	
	46		47					48		49		
50					51							

"Then was Jesus led up of the Spirit into the wilderness to be tempted of the devil." — Matt. 4:1.

NUMBER 9

THE FIRST DISCIPLES OF JESUS

HORIZONTAL

1 The third disciple
6 "and saith unto him, . . . me" John 1:43
11 Acid dye
12 "And he brought . . . to Jesus" John 1:42
13 Ephesians
14 "Then Jesus . . . , and saw them following" John 1:38
15 "Can there any . . . thing come out of Nazareth" John 1:46
17 Ages
18 "Who art thou? that we may give . . . answer" John 1:22
19 The (F. pl.)
22 Part of a circle
23 Left Guard
25 "thou . . . the King of Israel" John 1:49
26 "when thou wast under the fig . . . " John 1:48
27 Frustrate
29 In favor of
30 Parent Teacher Association
31 "Rabbi, thou art the . . . of God" John 1:49
32 "Thou art Simon the son of . . . " John 1:42
36 "and his . . . shall become a multitude" Gen. 48:19
37 "come down . . . my child die" John 4:49
38 "which to day is, and to morrow is cast into the . . . " Matt. 6:30
39 "of whom Moses . . . the law" John 1:45
40 "John . . . , and two of his disciples" John 1:35
41 "thou shalt be called . . . " John 1:42
46 City of Benjamin I Chron. 8:12
48 "Thou hast caused men to . . . over our heads" Ps. 66:12
49 "He saith unto them, . . . and see" John 1:39
51 "Philip findeth . . . " John 1:45
52 "They came and . . . where he dwelt" John 1:39

VERTICAL

1 Simon's other name
2 "it was about the tenth . . . " John 1:39
3 "Behold an . . . indeed, in whom is no guile" John 1:47
4 Waterfalls
5 Suffix denoting pertaining to
6 "I saw thee under the . . . tree" John 1:50
7 Combining form meaning relation to the shoulder
8 "Then was Jesus . . . up of the Spirit" Matt. 4:1
9 Opus
10 " . . . knowest thou me" John 1:48
16 "Philip was . . . Bethsaida" John 1:44
18 "men know that ye . . . my disciples, if ye have love" John 13:35
19 Slip
20 "so the last . . . shall be worse than the first" Matt. 27:64
21 "which is by interpretation, A . . . " John 1:42
22 "in the night . . . of Moab is laid waste" Isa. 15:1
24 "shewing the . . . tidings of the kingdom of God" Luke 8:1
28 "Hereafter ye shall see heaven . . . " John 1:51
32 "one . . . or one tittle shall in no wise pass" Matt. 5:18
33 Round molding (pl.)
34 Combining form meaning new
35 The first disciple
36 "He first findeth his own brother . . . " John 1:41
41 Small bed
42 President of the Royal Academy
43 Hebrew measure
44 Woman's name
45 "Philip saith unto him, Come and . . . " John 1:46
47 North America
50 Mother

1	2	3	4	5			6	7		8	9	10
11						12				13		
14							15		16			
17											18	
					19	20	21			22		
		23	24		25				26			
27	28				29							
	30				31				32	33	34	35
36					37				38			
39								40				
		41		42	43	44	45					
46	47			48					49		50	
51										52		

"And the two disciples heard him speak, and they followed Jesus."— John 1:37.

NUMBER 10

JESUS' FIRST MIRACLE

HORIZONTAL

1 "that . . . ye shall ask of the Father in my name" John 15:16
10 North American Indian tribe
11 Loiter
12 Southern state
13 "both Jesus was called, . . . his disciples" John 2:2
14 " . . . the waterpots with water" John 2:7
15 "Every man . . . the beginning doth set forth good wine" John 2:10
16 Second note of scale
17 "behold, a greater than Solomon is . . . " Luke 11:31
19 "though thou shouldest make thy nest as high as the . . . " Jer. 49:16
20 "And . . . saith unto them" John 2:8
21 "Jesus . . . unto her" John 2:4
23 A Benjamite I Chron. 7:12
24 "keep themselves from things offered to . . . " Acts 21:25
26 South America
27 A high mountain
28 Genus of plants
29 . . . Sinai
31 Combining form denoting an early time
32 A fish
33 Dialect of Eastern Assam
34 Rue
37 In the midst of Jews; we turned around
38 "His mother saith . . . the servants" John 2:5
40 "I go to prepare a place for . . . " John 14:2
42 "what have I to do with . . . " John 2:4
44 "no man putteth new wine into . . . bottles" Luke 5:37
46 "when men have well drunk, then that which is . . . " John 2:10
48 Waterbirds; herons, snipes, etc.
51 Place of first miracle
52 Rawhide thong
54 Brazilian coin
55 "even the Son of man which . . . in heaven" John 3:13
56 "no man can . . . these miracles" John 3:2
57 "And they bare . . . " John 2:8
58 Exodus
A saying of Jesus' mother is 1, 20, 21, 38, 40, 56, and 57 combined

VERTICAL

1 "They have no . . . " John 2:3
2 "When the ruler of the feast . . . tasted the water" John 2:9
3 "I . . . the light of the world" John 8:12
4 "bind the . . . of thine head upon thee" Ezek. 24:17
5 Sunday School
6 Highpriest and judge of Israel I Sam. 14:3
7 Manservant
8 One of David's wives II Sam. 3:5
9 "And there were set there six . . . " John 2:6
10 "the third day there was a . . . " John 2:1
12 "in Cana of . . . " John 2:1
14 "the governor of the . . . " John 2:8
17 "turned about with a very small . . . " Jas. 3:4
18 Recording Secretary
20 "mine . . . is not yet come" John 2:4
22 Iowa
25 " . . . out now, and bear unto the governor" John 2:8
29 "the . . . of Jesus was there" John 2:1
30 Turkish governor
33 "The . . . are a people not strong" Prov. 30:25
35 "thou hast kept the . . . wine until now" John 2:10
36 "the . . . of the feast" John 2:9
39 Whirlwind off the Faroe Islands
41 "Rabbi, thou art the . . . of God" John 1:49
43 Female sheep
45 To suffer (Scot.)
46 "knew not whence it . . . " John 2:9
47 Radical
49 Servant of Solomon Ezra 2:57
50 " . . . waterpots of stone" John 2:6
51 Number of Psalm beginning, "I will sing of mercy and judgment"
53 "marriage . . . Cana" John 2:1

■	1	2	3	4	5		6	7	8		■	9
10						■	11			■	12	
13			■		■	14				■	15	
16		■	17		18		■	19				
	■	20		■	21		22			■	23	
24	25				■	26		■	■	27		
28				■	29		■	30	■	■	31	
32			■	33		■	34		35	36		
37		■	38			39	■	40			■	
■	■	41	■	42			43	■	44		45	■
■	46		47			■	48	49				50
51				■	52	53			■	54		
55		■	56		■		■	57		■	58	

"This beginning of miracles did Jesus in Cana of Galilee, and manifested forth his glory." — John 2:11.

NUMBER 11

JESUS AND NICODEMUS

HORIZONTAL

1 ". . . God be with him" John 3:2
5 "Art thou . . . master of Israel" John 3:10
6 "no . . . hath ascended up to heaven" John 3:13
9 Tin
10 "all that handle the . . . " Ezek. 27:29
13 "For God . . . loved the world" John 3:16
14 Book of maps
16 "And . . . is the condemnation" John 3:19
19, 20, and 21 "Ye must . . . . " John 3:7
23 "Let us search and . . . our ways" Lam. 3:40
25 "I am the Lord . . . God" Ex. 20:2
26 "called the altar . . . " Josh. 22:34
28 Knight of the Red Cross
31 "I . . . God, even thy God" Ps. 50:7
32 "but . . . that believeth not is condemned already" John 3:18
34 "it . . . be that a prophet perish out of Jerusalem" Luke 13:33
37 "how that the blind . . . " Luke 7:22
38 Grand Recorder
40 "he that doeth truth cometh . . . the light" John 3:21
41 A Benjamite I Chron. 7:12
43 "ye . . . up also the wheat with them" Matt. 13:29
45 "Except a man be born of . . . and of the Spirit" John 3:5
48 "There was a man of . . . Pharisees" John 3:1
50 "righteous shine forth as the sun in the . . . of their Father" Matt. 13:43
53 Fan-leaved palms
55 Rumanian coin
56 "there is one . . . to the righteous, and to the wicked" Eccl. 9:2
57 "and purely purge away thy . . . " Isa. 1:25
59 "many knew him, and . . . afoot" Mark 6:33
60 "That which is born . . . the flesh is flesh" John 3:6
61 "thou art a teacher come from . . . " John 3:2
Our text is 1, 5, 6, 19, 20, 21, 32, 34, 37, 48, 50, 60, and 61 combined

VERTICAL

1 "he cannot . . . into the kingdom" John 3:5
2 Small, sour apple
3 River in Italy
4 Tantalum
7 " . . . Moses lifted up the serpent" John 3:14
8 "for . . . man can do these miracles" John 3:2
9 Son of Cush Gen. 10:7
11 Right
12 "came to Jesus by . . . " John 3:2
15 "even the . . . of man which is in heaven" John 3:13
17 Head covering
18 "Verily, verily, I . . . unto thee" John 3:3
22 " . . . Nicodemus" John 3:1
24 "and . . . receive not our witness" John 3:11
27 District of Columbia
28 "We speak that we do . . . " John 3:11
29 Royal Navy
30 Animals of South America
31 Latin and Anglo-Saxon diphthong
33 Self
35 "neither in this mountain, nor yet . . . Jerusalem" John 4:21
36 "What shall we say . . . " Rom. 7:7
37 Senior
39 "The seed is . . . under their clods" Joel 1:17
42 Unit of work
43 "a . . . of the Jews" John 3:1
44 "more highly . . . he ought to think" Rom. 12:3
46 Son of Ezer Gen. 36:27
47 "these miracles that thou . . . " John 3:2
49 Combining form signifying within
51 Dead Letter Office
52 "even so . . . the Son of man be lifted up" John 3:14
54 South Sea Island drink
57 "would that men should . . . to you" Matt. 7: 12
58 Royal Dragoons

	1		2		3	4		5		6	7	8
9					10		11		12		13	
14				15			16	17		18		
19			20					21				22
23		24						25				
		26	27		28	29	30				31	
32	33		34	35				36		37		
	38	39		40			41		42			
43			44		45	46					47	
		48		49		50				51		52
53	54									55		
56								57	58			
59				60			61				62	

"For God so loved the world, that he gave his only begotten Son, that whosoever believeth in him should not perish, but have everlasting life." — John 3:16.

NUMBER 12

THE WOMAN OF SAMARIA

HORIZONTAL

2 and 13 ". . . . . . of this water shall thirst again" John 4:13
9 Hebrew deity
10 "in their hands they shall . . . thee up" Matt. 4:6
11 Equality (comb. form)
13 See 2 across
17 Transpose
18 "springing up into everlasting . . . " John 4:14
20 Sunday School
21 "when they had . . . about five and twenty or thirty furlongs" John 6:19
23 "I have meat to eat that ye know not . . . " John 4:32
24 "But . . . hour cometh, and now is" John 4:23
26 "from whence then hast thou that living . . . " John 4:11
27 Bag
28 "Now Jacob's well . . . there" John 4:6
29 Lighted
30 "How is it . . . thou, being a Jew, askest drink" John 4:9
32 " . . . that speak unto thee am he" John 4:26
33 "true worshippers . . . worship the Father" John 4:23
35 "Sir, I perceive that thou . . . a prophet" John 4:19
37 Grand Tyler
38 Plural ending of nouns
40 The (Fr.)
41 " . . . me to drink" John 4:7
42 "thou wouldest have asked of . . . " John 4:10
44 2000 pounds
45 Royal Scottish Academy
47 Grandson of Benjamin I Chron. 7:7
49 Ephesians
51 " . . . be in him a well of water" John 5:14
53 " . . . , thou hast nothing to draw with" John 4:11
54 "and the well is . . . " John 4:11
56 Silkworm
57 Finial
58 "good were it for that man if he had . . . been born" Mark 14:21
59 "Sir, give me this water, that I . . . not" John 4:15
A saying of Jesus is 2, 13, 23, 24, 26, 30, 32, 33, 41, 42, 51, 58, and 59 combined

VERTICAL

1 Violoncello
3 Japanese sash
4 Reason
5 "and he was strong as the . . . " Amos 2:9
6 "how long will it be . . . they attain to innocency" Hosea 8:5
7 Japanese measure
8 "many more believed because of his own . . . " John 4:41
12 Aseptic
13 Defender of the Faith
14 To tat again
15 Rubbish
16 "thou art neither cold nor . . . " Rev. 3:15
19 " . . . thou knewest the gift of God" John 4:10
22 "our father Jacob, which gave us the . . . " John 4:12
25 House of Commons
26 "which art, and . . . , and art to come" Rev. 11:17
27 "wearied with his journey, . . . thus on the well" John 4:6
30 Jesus . . . with the woman of Samaria
31 Holy Roman Empire
34 Servant of Solomon Ezra 2:57
36 "repentance for the remission of . . . " Luke 3:3
37 Ancient city south of Gaza Gen. 10:19
39 "God is a . . . " John 4:24
41 "And he must needs . . . through Samaria" John 4:4
42 Place to which a portion of the Israelites were transported by Shalmaneser II Kings 17:6
43 Money hoarder
44 "he would have given . . . living water" John 4:10
46 Long cut
48 Tears
50 "not with ink and . . . write unto thee" III John 13
52 "Jesus saith unto . . . , Woman, believe me" John 4:21
55 Post village

1	■	2		3	4	5	6			7	■	8
9		■	■	10				■	■	11	12	
	■	13	14					15	16	■	17	
18	19			■	20		■	21		22		
23		■	24	25		■	26					■
■	■	27			■	28			■	29		
30	31			■	32	■	33		34			■
35			■	36	■	37		■		■	38	39
40		■	41				■	42		43	■	
	■	44			■	45	46		■	47	48	
49	50		■	51	52				■	53		
54			55	■	56				■	57		
■	58					■	59					

"God is a Spirit: and they that worship him must worship him in spirit and in truth." — John 4:24.

NUMBER 13

THE HEALING OF THE NOBLEMAN'S SON

HORIZONTAL

1 "I say unto one, . . . and he goeth" Luke 7:8
3 " . . . brother shall rise again" John 11:23
5 See 5 down
8 Place the miracle was performed
9 "Hereafter ye shall . . . heaven open" John 1:51
10 " . . . the father knew that it was at the same hour" John 4:53
11 Alderman
12 The cony of Scripture
14 "smote him there under the fifth . . . " II Sam. 3:27
15 A dessert
16 and 29 down "Sir, come down, . . . my child . . . " John 4:49
17 Grand Lodge
18 Hebrew deity
19 and 20 "where he . . . the water . . . " John 4:46
22 To tat again
23 "ye will . . . believe" John 4:48
24 Compass point
25 "O woman, great is . . . faith" Matt. 15:28
26 "whose . . . was sick" John 4:46
27 Lava
28 "And the Word was made flesh, and dwelt among . . . " John 1:14
29 Concerning
30 "as he was now going . . . " John 4:51
32 Doctor of Both Laws
34 Social musical parties
37 "would not lift up so . . . as his eyes unto heaven" Luke 18:13
39 "seventh hour the . . . left him" John 4:52
40 House of Commons
42 "I have meat to . . . that ye know not of" John 4:32
44 Answer
45 Small yellow bird
46 "the hour when he . . . to amend" John 4:52
47 Royal Navy
48 Buzz
49 Each
50 "he ever . . . to make intercession" Heb. 7:25
51 "ye . . . of this world" John 8:23
A saying of Jesus is 1, 3, 5, 25, 26, and 50 combined

VERTICAL

1 Cana of . . .
2 Wavy (Heraldry)
4 "When he . . . that Jesus was come out of Judaea" John 4:47
5 and 5 across "and he . . . his . . . " John 4:50
6 Diphthong
7 "there was a certain . . . " John 4:46
8 Place nobleman resided
9 Continent in Western Hemisphere
10 and 20 "Except ye see . . .s and . . . " John 4:48
12 "he was at the point of . . . " John 4:47
13 "Bring forth therefore fruits . . . for repentance" Matt. 3:8
19 Rugs
20 See 10 down
21 and 40 "father knew that . . . was at the same . . . " John 4:53
23 "so great faith, . . . , not in Israel" Matt. 8:10
26 "his . . .s met him" John 4:51
27 The end of law
28 United Daughters of the Confederacy
29 See 16 across
31 Bone
33 Country in Palestine (var.)
35 Often
36 Even (contr.)
38 See 41 down
40 See 21 down
41 and 38 " . . . down, and . . . his son" John 4:47
43 Tropical American cuckoo
46 "How can these things . . . " John 3:9
47 Second note in scale
48 Laughter sound

■	1	2	■	3	4		■	5	6		■	7
8				■		■	9			■	10	
11			■	12		13			■	14		
15			■	16			■		■	■	17	
18		■	19				■	■	20	21		
22					■		■	23			■	
24		■	25			■	26			■	27	
	■	28		■	■	29		■	30	31		
32	33		■	34	35			36			■	■
37			38	■	39					■	40	41
■		■	42	43		■	44			■	45	
46					■	47		■	■	48		
49		■	50						■	51		

"And the man believed the word that Jesus had spoken unto him, and he went his way." — John 4:50.

NUMBER 14

THE CALLING OF FOUR FISHERMEN AND THE MIRACLE OF FISHES

HORIZONTAL

1 " . . . me, and I will make you fishers of men" Matt. 4:19
6 Brother of John (One of the fishermen)
10 Adjective or noun suffix; last part of a mile
11 Northeast
12 Grandson of Esau Gen. 36:11
14 "Satan hath desired to have you, that he may . . . you as wheat" Luke 22:31
15 "and filled both the . . . , so that they began to sink" Luke 5:7
16 "their conscience seared with a . . . iron" I Tim. 4:2
17 "at thy word I will let . . . the net" Luke 5:5
19 Recede
21 "And he . . . down, and taught" Luke 5:3
23 Second note in scale
24 Railroad
26 "saw . . . ships standing by the lake" Luke 5:2
28 A fish
30 . . . Peter (another fisherman)
32 Month
33 "I will . . . you to become fishers of men" Mark 1:17
34 "walking by the . . . of Galilee" Matt. 4:18
35 "and . . . down your nets" Luke 5:4
36 Hosea (var.)
37 "from henceforth thou shalt catch . . . " Luke 5:10
38 Brother of Simon (another fisherman)
42 Seventh note
44 "Launch out into the . . . " Luke 5:4
46 Before (comb. form); poker stake
48 "the . . . of man hath power upon earth" Luke 5:24
49 "come down . . . my child die" John 4:49
50 "toiled all the . . . " Luke 5:5
51 "the fishermen were . . . out of them" Luke 5:2
52 "when he . . . left speaking" Luke 5:4
53 Plural ending of nouns

VERTICAL

1 "for they were . . . " Matt. 4:18
2 Medley
3 "straightway . . . their nets, and followed him" Matt. 4:20
4 "And going . . . from thence" Matt. 4:21
5 "Master, . . . have toiled" Luke 5:5
6 Brother of James (another fisherman)
7 Servant of Solomon Ezra 2:57
8 Geographical representation
9 Belonging to the Celts
13 Father of James and John
15 Compass point
17 "as it began to . . . toward the first day of the week" Matt. 28:1
18 Tribe of Indians
20 "and their net . . . " Luke 5:6
21 Portico
22 Odor (comb. form)
25 "The Lord is . . . indeed" Luke 24:34
27 "Jesus said unto Simon, Fear . . . " Luke 5:10
29 "Peter, and Andrew his brother, . . . a net into the sea" Matt. 4:18
31 "with Zebedee their father, . . . their nets" Matt. 4:21
32 "Come ye after . . . " Mark 1:17
37 Parsonage
39 Paradise
40 "and all that . . . with him" Luke 5:9
41 "when the sun was . . . , it was scorched" Mark 4:6
42 "he . . . unto Simon" Luke 5:4
43 "and were washing their . . . " Luke 5:2
45 Eye (Scot.)
47 "thrust out a little from . . . land" Luke 5:3
50 North America

1	2	3		4	5		6	7	8	9		
10				11			12					13
14						15						
16				17	18					19	20	
			21						22		23	
24	25		26				27		28	29		
30		31				32			33			
	34				35				36			
37												
38				39	40		41		42			43
				44		45			46		47	
48				49				50				
		51					52				53	

"And Jesus said unto Simon, Fear not; from henceforth thou shalt catch men." — Luke 5:10.

NUMBER 15

HEALING A PARALYTIC

HORIZONTAL

2 "the . . . of man hath power on earth to forgive sins" Mark 2:10
4 "I will; . . . thou clean" Mark 1:41
6 "there were certain . . . the scribes sitting there" Mark 2:6
8 "all that handle the . . . " Ezek. 27:29
10 "Who can forgive sins, but God . . . " Luke 5:21
12 "and . . . unto thine house" Matt. 9:6
13 "lying . . . a bed" Matt. 9:2
15 Month in Hebrew calendar
17 "When Jesus saw their . . . , he said" Mark 2:5
21 Small yellow birds (Hawaiian)
22 "there is none . . . but one, that is, God" Matt. 19:17
23 "Be of good . . . ; it is I" Matt. 14:27
24 Cry, as a cat
25 Royal Marines
26 "they could . . . come nigh unto him for the press" Mark 2:4
27 "immediately he . . . up before them" Luke 5:25
29 "every good . . . bringeth forth good fruit" Matt. 7:17
31 "Wherefore think . . . evil in your hearts" Matt. 9:4
33 Having large, incased nostrils
35 Spain
36 "and . . . Father which seeth in secret" Matt. 6:4
38 "baptized of him in Jordan, confessing their . . . " Matt. 3:6
39 "thou shalt not . . . as the hypocrites are" Matt. 6:5
40 Sift (Prov. Eng.)
41 Stimulating narcotic
42 "the power of the Lord was present to . . . them" Luke 5:17
44 "thou shalt stand by the river's . . . against he come" Ex. 7:15
46 "glorified God, which . . . given such power unto men" Matt. 9:8
47 Trees of the olive family
49 Thing
50 "they sought means to bring him, . . . " Luke 5:18
51 "forgive, and ye shall be . . . " Luke 6:37
52 "Give to every man that asketh of . . . " Luke 6:30
A saying of Jesus is 2, 4, 6, 22, 23, 36, 38, 39, 51, and 52 combined

VERTICAL

1 "there was no . . . to receive them" Mark 2:2
2 Senior
3 North America
4 Buyer's option
5 "so shall it be in the . . . of this world" Matt. 13:40
7 "they went upon the . . . , and let him down" Luke 5:19
9 "seweth a piece of new cloth on . . . old garment" Mark 2:21
11 "they . . . down the bed" Mark 2:4
14 Old Italian coin
16 "which was . . . of four" Mark 2:3
17 Number of men that carried the paralytic
18 The same
19 His Catholic Majesty
20 "reasoning in their . . . " Mark 2:6
22 Southern state
24 "and go thy . . . into thine house" Mark 2:11
25 "Why . . . ye these things in your hearts" Mark 2:8
28 Tin
29 Kind of fish
30 Eye (Scot.)
32 Summer (Fr.)
34 "a man . . . of the palsy" Matt. 9:2
35 "casting a net into the . . . " Mark 1:16
37 Son of Ezra I Chron. 4:18
39 "Arise, and take up thy . . . " Mark 2:11
40 "they uncovered the . . . where he was" Mark 2:4
41 Crown of India
42 "thou . . . the words of eternal life" John 6:68
43 "precept upon precept; . . . upon . . . " Isa. 28:10
45 "all our righteousnesses are as filthy . . .s" Isa. 64:6
46 "again . . . entered into Capernaum" Mark 2:1
48 "and, . . . I am with you alway" Matt. 28:20
49 Royal Navy
50 Namely

1	■	2		3	■	4	5	■	6		■	7
8	9		■	10	11				■	■	12	
13		■	14	■		■		■	15	16	■	
	■	17		18		19	■	20	■	21		
■	22				■	23					■	
24				■	25		■		■	26		
	■	27		28		■	29		30		■	
31	32	■	■	33		34				■	35	
■	36	37		■	38				■	39		■
40			■	41				■	42			43
	■	44	45				■	46			■	
47	48			■	■	■	49			■	50	
51								■	52			

"But that ye may know that the Son of man hath power on earth to forgive sins (then saith he to the sick of the palsy), Arise, take up thy bed, and go unto thine house." — Matt. 9:6.

NUMBER 16

THE RAISING OF THE DAUGHTER OF JAIRUS

HORIZONTAL

1 "come and lay thy . . . on her" Mark 5:23
4 "besought him that he would . . . into his house" Luke 8:41
8 "While . . . yet spake" Mark 5:35
9 "and she shall . . . made whole" Luke 8:50
10 "she is . . . dead, but sleepeth" Luke 8:52
11 "when he had put them . . . out" Mark 5:40
13 Ancestor of Jesus Luke 3:28
14 "My . . . daughter lieth" Mark 5:23
15 "we have done that which was our . . . to do" Luke 17:10
18 District of Columbia
19 "And they . . . him to scorn" Mark 5:40
21 "Why make ye this ado, and . . . " Mark 5:39
24 "how long will it be . . . they attain to innocency" Hos. 8:5
26 Contend
27 Of
28 "it is I; be not . . . " Mark 6:50
32 "Why troublest thou the . . . any further" Mark 5:35
33 Nahum
35 Pronoun
39 "he saith unto the . . . of the synagogue" Mark 5:36
42 "suffered no man to . . . him, save Peter, and James, and John" Mark 5:37
46 Weblike tissue
47 Girl's name
48 "who can forgive sins but God . . . " Mark 2:7
49 "Fear not: . . . only, and she shall be made whole" Luke 8:50
50 Editors
51 " . . . soon . . . Jesus heard the word" Mark 5:36
52 "whosoever will save his life shall . . . it" Mark 8:35
53 " . . . pray thee" Mark 5:23

VERTICAL

1 "And . . . spirit came again" Luke 8:55
2 New Brunswick
3 "lieth at the point of . . . " Mark 5:23
4 "a cup of . . . water" Matt. 10:42
5 Pertaining to the ear
6 "commanded that something should be given her to . . . " Mark 5:43
7 "the damsel is not dead, but . . . " Mark 5:39
8 "that she may be . . . " Mark 5:23
12 Low Latin
15 "till he should pay all that was . . . unto him" Matt. 18:34
16 Half ugly
17 "about twelve . . . of age" Luke 8:42
20 "where two or three . . . gathered together" Matt. 18:20
22 "My daughter is . . . now dead" Matt. 9:18
23 East Indies
25 "When he speaketh a . . . , he speaketh of his own" John 8:44
28 "But I know him: for I . . . from him" John 7:29
29 "And the . . . hereof went abroad into all that land" Matt. 9:26
30 "and . . . the sacrifices of the dead" Ps. 106:28
31 Physician
34 "And straightway the damsel . . . , and walked" Mark 5:42
36 General inclination
37 Pouts (colloq.)
38 Plant used in medicine (pl.)
40 "come and . . . thy hand upon her" Matt. 9:18
41 "and he took one of his . . . , and closed up the flesh" Gen. 2:21
42 "when he saw him, he . . . at his feet" Mark 5:22
43 Mixture
44 "and she shall . . . " Mark 5:23
45 "My name is Legion: for . . . are many" Mark 5:9
46 "upon the great . . . of their right foot" Ex. 29:20

	1		2	3			4	5		6		7
8			9			10				11	12	
13							14					
		15	16		17		18					
19	20								21	22	23	
24							25			26		
27			28	29		30		31				
			32							33	34	
35	36	37							38			
	39		40		41		42	43		44		45
46							47					
48					49							
50				51			52					53

"And Jesus went with him; and much people followed him, and thronged him." — Mark 5:24.

NUMBER 17

JESUS HEALING A LAME MAN ON THE SABBATH

HORIZONTAL

1 Township
3 "it is not . . . for thee to carry thy bed" John 5:10
9 "Behold, . . . art made whole" John 5:14
11 "but . . . I am coming, another steppeth down" John 5:7
13 "and . . . up his bed" John 5:9
14 "shaken together, and running . . . " Luke 6:38
15 "had been now . . . long time in that case" John 5:6
16 The (Fr.)
17 "ye have neither heard his voice at any time, . . . seen his shape" John 5:37
19 "For the Father loveth the . . . " John 5:20
22 "said unto thee, Take up thy bed, and . . . " John 5:12
23 Israelite of the tribe of Asher I Chron. 7:34
25 "a certain . . . was there" John 5:5
27 "That Christ cometh of the . . . of David" John 7:42
28 Girl's name
30 "When Jesus . . . him lie" John 5:6
33 and 40 down "of . . . , . . . , withered, waiting for the moving of the water" John 5:3
35 Southern state
36 "fled before the men of . . . " Josh. 7:4
39 "and on the same . . . was the sabbath" John 5:9
40 "said unto . . . that was cured" John 5:10
41 "They reel to and . . . , and stagger" Ps. 107:27
43 "he that was . . . wist not who it was" John 5:13
45 Sphere
47 Month in Hebrew calendar
49 Thallium
50 " . . . , take up thy bed, and walk" John 5:8
51 "to put . . . into the pool" John 5:7
52 "and troubled the . . . " John 5:4
53 Sleigh

VERTICAL

1 Though
2 "angel went down at a certain season into the . . . " John 5:4
4 The last of law
5 "immediately the man was made . . . " John 5:9
6 "having . . . porches" John 5:2
7 A tree
8 Genus of the fish-lice family
9 Size of shot
10 United Kingdom
12 "My Father worketh hitherto, and I . . . " John 5:17
18 "putteth new wine into . . . bottles" Luke 5:37
19 "It is the . . . day" John 5:10
20 Son of Zerubbabel I Chron. 3:20
21 Unless (Lat.)
22 "Why could not . . . cast him out" Mark 9:28
26 Nova Scotia
27 Southwest
29 "and the lizard, and the . . . , and the mole" Lev. 11:30
31 "there is . . . Jerusalem, by the sheep market a pool" John 5:2
32 "In these . . . a great multitude of impotent folk" John 5:3
34 Ten cents
35 General Assembly
37 "there was a feast . . . the Jews" John 5:1
38 "lest a . . . thing come unto thee" John 5:14
40 See 33 across
42 Perplex
44 Greek letter
46 "same said unto me, Take up thy . . . , and walk" John 5:11
48 "Wilt thou . . . made whole" John 6:6
50 Recording Secretary

"Verily, verily, I say unto you, He that heareth my word, and believeth on him that sent me, hath everlasting life, and shall not come into condemnation; but is passed from death unto life." — John 5:24.

NUMBER 18

JESUS HEALS A MAN WITH A WITHERED HAND ON THE SABBATH

HORIZONTAL

1 "the Son of man . . . Lord also of the sabbath" Luke 6:5
3 "he entered into the . . . and taught" Luke 6:6
10 "and said . . . the man" Luke 6:8
11 Diphthong; of age
12 "And he arose and . . . forth" Luke 6:8
13 Correct
14 "And all that handle the . . . " Ezek. 27:29
16 "Rise . . . , and stand" Luke 6:8
18 " . . . will ask you one thing" Luke 6:9
19 Exclamation of inquiry
21 Dead Letter Office
22 Seventh note
23 "whether he would heal on the sabbath . . . " Luke 6:7
26 "and lift it . . . " Matt. 12:11
28 Devil
31 Behaved
34 "stand forth . . . the midst" Luke 6:8
36 Among
37 "his hand was restored . . . as the other" Luke 6:10
38 Relative
39 "if it . . . into a pit on the sabbath day" Matt. 12:11
41 Home of Abram Gen. 11:31
42 " . . . to do evil" Luke 6:9
44 Missouri
46 "to save . . . , or to destroy it" Luke 6:9
49 Egyptian sun god
50 "that they might find . . . accusation against him" Luke 6:7
51 "and he was strong as the . . . " Amos 2:9
53 "like as . . . other" Matt. 12:13
55 Northeast
56 "he said unto the man, . . . forth thy hand" Luke 6:10

VERTICAL

1 "And . . . came to pass" Luke 6:6
2 "And he did . . . " Luke 6:10
3 and 4 "But whom . . . . . . that I am" Luke 9:20
5 "And they . . . him, saying, Is it" Matt. 12:10
6 Grand Tyler
7 Small yellow bird
8 "Is it lawful on the sabbath days to do . . . " Luke 6:9
9 Freehold
15 "And looking . . . about upon them all, he said" Luke 6:10
16 "being interpreted is, God with . . . " Matt. 1:23
17 Small firearm
20 "man which . . . his hand withered" Matt. 12:10
24 "his parents went to Jerusalem every . . . at the feast" Luke 2:41
25 "it is . . . to do well on the sabbath days" Matt. 12:12
26 Poem
27 Titanium
29 Madame
30 "Give us of your . . . ; for our lamps are gone out" Matt. 25:8
32 "sitting in his . . . read Esaias the prophet" Acts 8:28
33 Measure of length
35 "Take therefore . . . thought for the morrow" Matt. 6:34
40 "And he stretched it . . . " Matt. 12:13
43 Hurrah
44 "How much then is a . . . better than a sheep" Matt. 12:12
45 "that shall have . . . sheep" Matt. 12:11
47 "when he was now not . . . from the house" Luke 7:6
48 To add to
52 . . . Luke
54 Half an em

"Wherefore it is lawful to do well on the sabbath days." — Matt. 12:12.

NUMBER 19

THE BEATITUDES

HORIZONTAL

1 "Blessed are they that . . . : for they shall be comforted" Matt. 5:4
5 Spain
7 "and shall . . . all manner of evil against you falsely" Matt. 5:11
10 "Whence shall we buy bread, that these may . . . " John 6:5
11 Before, a combining form; poker stake
13 "that they may . . . your good works" Matt. 5:16
14 Royal Society of Edinburgh
15 and 30 "Blessed are the . . . in . . . : for theirs is the kingdom of heaven" Matt. 5:3
16 "the . . . of violence is in their hands" Isa. 59:6
18 Genus of animals
19 "and of . . . that taketh away thy goods ask them not again" Luke 6:30
22 "Blessed are ye, when men shall . . . you, and persecute you" Matt. 5:11
24 "and when he was . . . " Matt. 5:1
25 "ships of Tarshish bringing gold, and silver, ivory, and . . . , and peacocks" II Chron. 9:21
26 and 48 "Blessed are they which do . . . and . . . after righteousness" Matt. 5:6
27 One third of supper
28 "And as he entered into a certain village, there . . . him ten men" Luke 17:12
30 See 15 across
32 Plural ending of nouns
35 "how long will it be . . . thou be quiet" Jer. 47:6
36 "Blessed are the . . . : for they shall be called the children of God" Matt. 5:9
38 A fish (Hawaiian)
39 Make angry
41 "Rejoice, and be exceeding glad: for . . . is your reward in heaven" Matt. 5:12
45 "his disciples came . . . him" Matt. 5:1
47 First woman
48 See 26 across

VERTICAL

1 "Blessed are the . . . : for they shall obtain mercy" Matt. 5:7
2 Kiln
3 Indian
4 Short sleep
5 Backless chair
6 "Blessed are they which are . . . for righteousness' sake" Matt. 5:10
7 Sunday School
8 Diphthong
9 " . . . are the light of the world" Matt. 5:14
12 To us (L.)
17 To pepper again
19 Here lies (L.)
20 Namely
21 . . . of Olives
22 "all our righteousnesses are as filthy . . . " Isa. 64:6
23 Adding ly to this means truly
27 " . . . , I perceive that thou art a prophet" John 4:19
28 "Blessed are the . . . : for they shall inherit the earth" Matt. 5:5
29 Jacob's brother
31 Brownish substance exuding from certain plants
33 See 36 down
34 Father
36 and 33 "Blessed are the . . . in . . . : for they shall see God" Matt. 5:8
37 Put to flight
40 Lieutenant
42 Exclamation of inquiry
43 Joshua was defeated at . . . Josh. 7:5
44 Transpose
46 "A city that is set . . . a hill cannot be hid" Matt. 5:14

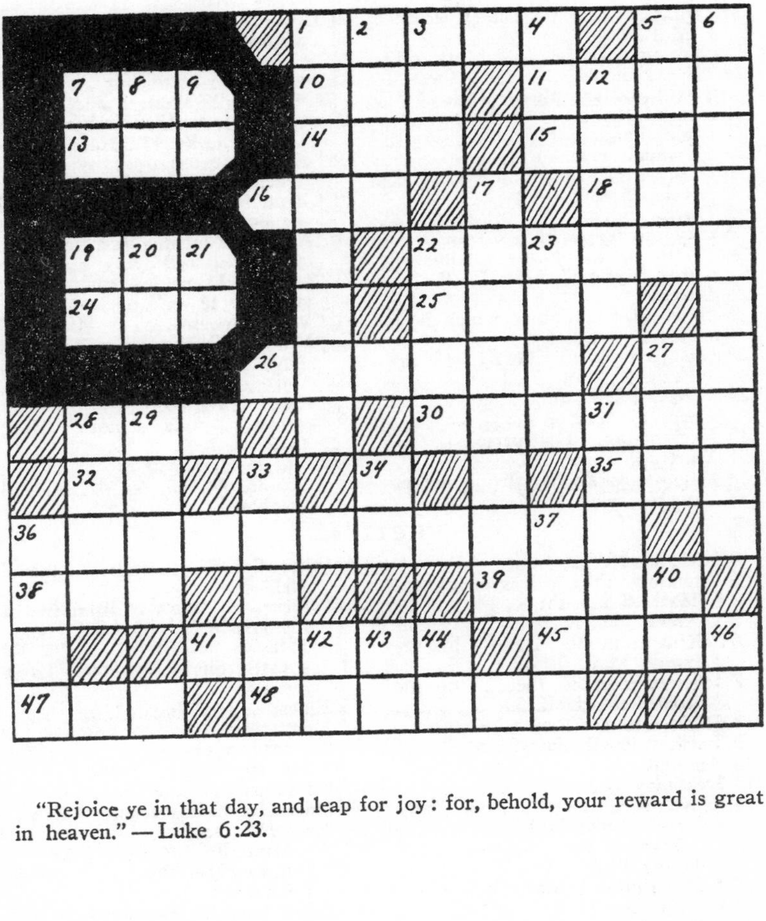

"Rejoice ye in that day, and leap for joy: for, behold, your reward is great in heaven." — Luke 6:23.

NUMBER 20

THE LORD'S PRAYER

HORIZONTAL

1 " . . . when ye pray, use not vain repetitions" Matt. 6:7
4 "and the . . . , and the glory, for ever" Matt. 6:13
9 Scold
11 "what . . . right hand doeth" Matt. 6:3
12 "For thine is the . . ." Matt. 6:13
14 "If I should . . . with thee, I will not deny thee" Mark 14:31
16 South Dakota
17 Man's name
19 Hawaiian lava
20 "I am . . . in my Father's name" John 5:43
22 Dove's call
23 City of Benjamin I Chron. 8:12
24 "With a great . . . obtained I this freedom" Acts 22:28
25 Doctor
26 "pray to . . . Father which is in secret" Matt. 6:6
28 "he that doeth the . . . of my Father" Matt. 7:21
29 "That thine alms may . . . in secret" Matt. 6:4
30 Exclamation of surprise
31 Yard
32 Daughter of Zachariah and mother of Hezekiah II Kings 18:2
34 and 38 "Thy will be . . . , as in heaven, so in . . . " Luke 11:2
36 "of your Father which is . . . heaven" Matt. 6:1
38 See 34 across
40 Unit of work
42 Last word of prayer
44 ". . . the hypocrites do" Matt. 6:2
45 "nor by the earth; for . . . is his footstool" Matt. 5:35
46 and 47 "unto thy Father which . . . . . . secret" Matt. 6:18
49 "given to hospitality, . . . to teach" I Tim. 3:2
50 Chapter in Matt. beginning "And he entered into a ship"
51 "After this manner therefore . . . ye" Matt. 6:9
53 "but deliver . . . from evil" Matt. 6:13
54 "which art in . . . " Matt. 6:9
57 "Many will say to . . . in that day" Matt. 7:22
58 "And . . . us not into temptation" Matt. 6:13
59 "as we . . . our debtors" Matt. 6:12
Our text is 11, 12, 20, 26, 28, 29, 34, 36, 38, 44, 45, 46, 47, and 54 combined

VERTICAL

2 Rodent of West Indies
3 "standing in . . . synagogues" Matt. 6:5
5 Correct
6 "he shall in no . . . lose his reward" Matt. 10:42
7 "the harvest is the . . . of the world" Matt. 13:39
8 Right Guard
9 Back, a combining form
10 Amount
13 Destiny
14 "Give us . . . by . . . our daily bread" Luke 11:3
15 "This is my beloved . . . " Matt. 3:17
18 " . . . Father" Matt. 6:9
20 Coquettish
21 Cut
22 Ancient Scotch or Irish monks
24 Cunning
25 "And forgive us our . . .s" Matt. 6:12
26 Though
27 "whatsoever things are . . . " Phil. 4:8
29 "shut the doors, and . . . them" Neh. 7:3
30 "wherewith the . . . number of them is to be redeemed" Num. 3:48
33 Jesus the Savior of Men (Latin initials)
35 Eldest son of Judah Gen. 38:3
37 North America
39 "it hath been said, . . . eye for . . . eye" Matt. 5:38
41 " . . . us this day" Matt. 6:11
43 One who makes friends easily
44 An arched roof
47 A Benjamite I Chron. 7:12
48 "Hallowed be thy . . . " Matt. 6:9
49 "shall bore his ear through with an . . . " Ex. 21:6
50 Three fifths ivory
52 "your Father knoweth what things . . . have need of" Matt. 6:8
54 . . . kf is handkerchief
55 Africa
56 No good

1	2	3		4	5	6	7	8		9	10	
	11				12				13			
14				15		16			17			18
19			20		21			22				
			23				24				25	
	26	27			28					29		
30							31			32		33
34			35		36	37		38	39			
		40		41		42	43					
	44			45			46			47	48	
49						50			51			52
53			54		55			56			57	
58					59							

"But thou, when thou prayest, enter into thy closet, and when thou hast shut thy door, pray to thy Father which is in secret; and thy Father which seeth in secret shall reward thee openly." — Matt. 6:6.

NUMBER 21

THE ANOINTING WITH OIL

HORIZONTAL

1 "Thou hast . . . judged" Luke 7:43
6 "if he were a prophet, would have . . . who" Luke 7:39
10 Japanese measure
11 " . . . , every one that thirsteth" Isa. 55:1
12 Seventh note in scale
13 Suffix, forming adjectives
14 "he, to whom he . . . most" Luke 7:43
16 "Her . . . , which are many, are forgiven" Luke 7:47
17 " . . . when they had nothing to pay" Luke 7:42
18 "hath washed my feet with . . . " Luke 7:44
19 "and . . . other fifty" Luke 7:41
21 "to whom little . . . forgiven" Luke 7:47
22 "I . . . God, even thy God" Ps. 50:7
23 Terbium
26 "and sat down to . . . " Luke 7:36
28 Grief
30 "the . . . owed five hundred pence" Luke 7:41
31 "loose his . . . or his ass from the stall" Luke 13:15
32 . . . Luke
34 Compass point
36 "Thou gavest . . . no kiss" Luke 7:45
37 "did wipe them with the . . .s of her head" Luke 7:38
39 "And, behold, a . . . in the city" Luke 7:37
44 "knew that Jesus sat . . . meat" Luke 7:37
45 Japanese sash
46 "went into the Pharisee's . . . " Luke 7:36
47 "and kissed his . . . " Luke 7:38
49 National Recovery Administration
51 Civil Service
53 "every . . . is known by his own fruit" Luke 6:44
54 " . . . thee behind me, Satan" Luke 4:8
55 "My . . . with oil thou didst not anoint" Luke 7:46

VERTICAL

2 "fill his skin with barbed . . . " Job 41:7
3 "he shall . . . himself" Luke 12:37
4 "Who is this . . . forgiveth sins also" Luke 7:49
5 and 41 "for she . . . . . . " Luke 7:47
6 "hath not ceased to . . . my feet" Luke 7:45
7 "hath anointed my feet with . . . " Luke 7:46
8 "began to . . . his feet with tears" Luke 7:38
9 North latitude
14 "Thy . . . hath saved thee" Luke 7:50
15 Babylonian deity
20 "that he would . . . with him" Luke 7:36
22 Minor prophet
23 "which had . . . debtors" Luke 7:41
24 "an alabaster . . . of ointment" Luke 7:37
25 "I have . . . to say unto thee" Luke 7:40
27 Of age (L.)
29 "stood at his feet behind him . . . " Luke 7:38
33 " . . . in peace" Luke 7:50
34 "and made me a polished . . . " Isa. 49:2
35 "thou gavest me no . . . for my feet" Luke 7:44
38 Mechanical repetition
40 Small yellow bird
41 See 5 down
42 South African fox
43 New England
48 Eye (Scot.)
50 Second note in scale
52 Newspaper item

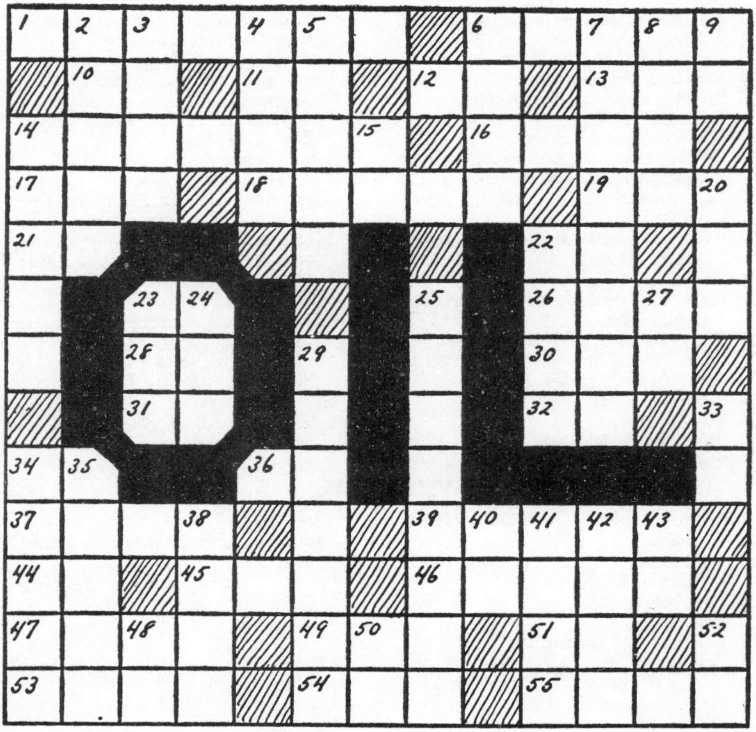

"And he said to the woman, Thy faith hath saved thee; go in peace."—Luke 7:50.

NUMBER 22

THE PARABLE OF THE SOWER

HORIZONTAL

1 " . . . there went out a sower to sow" Mark 4:3
6 "the thorns sprung up, and . . . them" Matt. 13:7
10 "because they had no deepness of . . . " Matt. 13:5
12 Grandson of Benjamin I Chron. 7:7
13 Capital of Moab Num. 21:28
14 Small European fish
15 "And some fell among . . . " Matt. 13:7
18 Recording Secretary
20 "Pharisees began to . . . him vehemently" (pl.) Luke 11:53
22 "but dureth for . . . while" Matt. 13:21
23 "The . . . soweth the word" Mark 4:14
26 Township
28 "and the deceitfulness of riches, choke the . . . " Matt. 13:22
29 Song by one person
31 "the . . . of my goods I give to the poor" Luke 19:8
34 Grain
36 Meridian
37 "Yet hath he not . . . in himself" Matt. 13:21
39 "he that received . . . into the good ground" Matt. 13:23
41 Fourth note in scale
42 and 64 "A sower . . . out to . . . his seed" Luke 8:5
44 "and bringeth . . . , some an hundredfold, some sixty, some thirty" Matt. 13:23
47 Second son of Adam Gen. 4:2
48 "and anon with . . . receiveth it" Matt. 13:20
50 "and the . . . of this world" Matt. 13:22
51 Low Latin
52 . . . Matthew
54 "for my life laid down their own . . . " Rom. 16:4
56 Meadow
58 "some seeds fell by the . . . side" Matt. 13:4
60 Hosea (var.)
62 "the whole multitude . . . on the shore" Matt. 13:2
63 "Who hath ears . . . hear, let him hear" Matt. 13:9
64 See 42 across
Our text is 1, 22, 23, 42, 44, 63, and 64 combined

VERTICAL

1 "which also . . . fruit" Matt. 13:23
2 "and your . . . , for they hear" Matt. 13:16
3 Part of a day
4 Aural
5 Doctor of Humanities
7 "to know the mysteries of the . . . of heaven" Matt. 13:11
8 Belonging to the Celts
9 Didymium
11 "and understandeth . . . not" Matt. 13:19
16 " . . . Father which art in heaven" Matt. 6:9
17 Means of travel
19 "But other fell into . . . ground" Matt. 13:8
21 "when the sun was up, they were . . . " Matt. 13:6
23 Compass point
24 Writer
25 "fall by the . . . of the sword" Luke 21:24
27 "he spake many things unto them in . . . , saying" Matt. 13:3
30 The (F.)
32 "and, . . . I am with you alway" Matt. 28:20
33 "the . . . came and devoured them up" Matt. 13:4
35 Reference
38 Tellurium
39 "Some fell upon . . . places" Matt. 13:5
40 Cuts off
41 "in time of temptation . . . away" Luke 8:13
43 Eastern state
45 Levels with the ground
46 Transpose
49 "Hear . . . therefore the parable of the sower" Matt. 13:18
53 "No servant can serve . . . masters" Luke 16:13
55 Dove's call
57 "could not come . . . him for the press" Luke 8:19
59 Newspaper item
61 Relating to an early period of time, a combining form

1	2	3	4	5			6			7	8	9
10						11				12		
13			14			15		16	17			
18					19			20				21
		22		23		24	25					
26	27			28					29		30	
31		32	33				34	35		36		
	37			38		39			40			
41			42		43			44		45	46	
47					48		49		50			
51			52	53		54		55				
56		57		58	59			60			61	
	62						63			64		

"But other fell into good ground, and brought forth fruit, some an hundredfold, some sixtyfold, some thirtyfold." — Matt. 13:8.

NUMBER 23

THE PARABLE OF THE TARES

HORIZONTAL

1 " . . . when the blade was sprung up" Matt. 13:26
3 "that we go and . . . them up" Matt. 13:28
9 "righteous shine forth as the . . . " Matt. 13:43
10 Estate
11 Mother
12 "Rabbi, thou . . . the Son of God" John 1:49
13 "and them which . . . iniquity" Matt. 13:41
14 One who reels thread
16 Bite
18 Female deer
19 Month
20 Memento
22 "Another parable put he forth unto them, . . .ing" Matt. 13:24
24 Compass point
25 "called the altar . . . " Josh. 22:34
26 Kind of fish
28 Cry for help
29 "field is . . . world" Matt. 13:38
30 "sowed tares among the . . . " Matt. 13:25
32 River in Italy
34 " . . . therefore the tares are gathered" Matt. 13:40
35 Exclamation of inquiry
37 "shall send . . . his angels" Matt. 13:41
40 "which sowed good . . . in his field" Matt. 13:24
42 "ye . . . up also the wheat with them" Matt. 13:29
43 Cow's call
44 Dialect of Eastern Assam
45 Copper coin
47 . . . Lisa
49 Verb neuter
50 Small bundle of straw
52 Data
54 "blessed are your eyes, for they . . . " Matt. 13:16
55 "cast them . . . a furnace of fire" Matt. 13:42
56 "that they may behold . . . glory" John 17:24
57 "which neither have storehouse nor . . . " Luke 12:24
Our text is 1, 3, 29, 30, 55, 56, and 57 combined

VERTICAL

1 "gathered and . . . in the fire" Matt. 13:40
2 "grow together . . . the harvest" Matt. 13:30
3 "the . . . seed are the children of the kingdom" Matt. 13:38
4 "even as I . . . not of the world" John 17:16
5 "from whence then hath it . . . " Matt. 13:27
6 Hasten
7 "his . . . came and sowed tares" Matt. 13:25
8 "in the time of . . . " Matt. 13:30
9 Continent in Western Hemisphere
10 Doctor of Divinity
11 "I in them, and thou in . . . " John 17:23
15 "And, . . . the angel of the Lord came upon them" Luke 2:9
17 Importance
20 "and the . . . are the angels" Matt. 13:39
21 Intimation
23 Greek god of war
24 "just persons, which need . . . repentance" Luke 15:7
27 The end of law
28 Ladder (Prov. Eng.)
31 Laughter sound
33 Man's name
36 "The kingdom of . . . is likened" Matt. 13:24
37 "and brought forth . . . " Matt. 13:26
38 Small yellow bird
39 Frolic
40 "didst not thou . . . good seed" Matt. 13:27
41 "An enemy hath . . . this" Matt. 13:28
43 "He that soweth the good seed is the Son of . . . " Matt. 13:37
46 "and ye are not your . . . " I Cor. 6:19
48 "But he said, . . . ; lest while ye gather" Matt. 13:29
51 " . . . shall it be in the end of this world" Matt. 13:40
53 Month in Hebrew calendar
54 Senior

	1	2			3	4	5	6	7			8
9				10							11	
12				13			14			15		
	16		17		18				19			
20				21			22	23			24	
25			26			27				28		
		29				30	31					
32					33		34			35	36	
		37	38	39					40			41
		42					43				44	
45	46			47		48					49	
	50		51			52		53		54		
55					56			57				

"Then shall the righteous shine forth as the sun in the kingdom of their Father." — Matt. 13:43.

NUMBER 24

JESUS STILLS A TEMPEST

HORIZONTAL

2 " . . . shall we escape, if we neglect so great salvation" Heb. 2:3
5 "Where . . . your faith" Luke 8:25
7 "so that . . . was now full" Mark 4:37
10 For example
12 "he went into a ship with his . . .s" Luke 8:22
14 A compost heap
15 Blot out
16 Pair
17 Endows
20 The (F.)
21 "put him into the garden of . . . " Gen. 2:15
24 Bachelor of Arts
25 " . . . unto you, ye blind guides" Matt. 23:16
26 To set again
27 "and said unto the . . . , Peace, be still" Mark 4:39
29 "insomuch . . . the ship was covered with the waves" Matt. 8:24
31 and 58 "O . . . of little . . . " Matt. 8:26
32 "shall be taken even that which he seemeth to . . . " Luke 8:18
34 . . . Mark
36 Recording Secretary
38 "If any man among you . . . to be religious" Jas. 1:26
40 Kind of antelope
41 Laughter sound
43 Reverences
45 Road
46 "And he arose, and . . . the wind" Mark 4:39
48 Promissory note
49 Even (cont.)
51 "according to all the . . .s of it" Num. 9:3
52 See 39 down
53 "Then he . . . , and rebuked the winds" Matt. 8:26
55 "And the wind . . .d" Mark 4:39
57 "so great faith, . . . not in Israel" Luke 7:9
58 See 31 across
59 Senior
Saying of Jesus is 2, 5, 7, 29, 31, 32, 57, and 58 combined

VERTICAL

1 "there arose a great . . . in the sea" Matt. 8:24
3 Poem
4 "there arose a great storm of . . . " Mark 4:37
5 Suffix meaning dealing with
6 "Let us pass over unto the other . . . " Mark 4:35
7 "Love worketh no . . . to his neighbour" Rom. 13:10 (pl.)
8 Golf mound
9 " . . . on a pillow" Mark 4:38
11 "he shall . . . himself, and make them to sit down" Luke 12:37
13 "carest thou not that we . . . " Mark 4:38
18 "even the wind and the sea . . . him" Mark 4:41
19 "and they were filled with . . . " Luke 8:23
20 " . . . , I have told you" Matt. 28:7
22 Age
23 "And they straightway left their . . . , and followed him" Matt. 4:20
25 "the . . . beat into the ship" Mark 4:37
28 "mean not that other men be . . . , and ye burdened" II Cor. 8:13
30 "he was in the . . . part of the ship" Mark 4:38
33 Eye (Scot.)
35 "And . . . were also with him other little ships" Mark 4:36
37 "persecution ariseth for the word's . . . " Mark 4:17
39 and 52 across "What . . . of . . . is this" Mark 4:41
40 "there was a . . . calm" Mark 4:39
42 Mother of Hezekiah II Kings 18:2
44 "Lord, save us: . . . perish" Matt. 8:25
47 Rodent of the West Indies
48 "Now it came to . . . on a certain day" Luke 8:22
50 Not
52 Mother
54 "Why are ye . . . fearful" Mark 4:40
55 A penny
56 Exclamation of inquiry

1	■	2	3	4	■	5	6	■	7	8	■	9
10	11	■	12					13			■	
14					■	■	15				■	
16		■	■	17	18	19				■	20	
21		22	23	■	24		■		■	25		
	■	26					■	27	28		■	
29	30			■	31		■	32			33	■
■		■	34	35	■	36	37	■	38			39
40			■	41	42	■	43	44			■	
45		■	46			47				■	48	
49		50	■	51				■	■	52		
53			54		■		■	55	56			
	■	57		■	58					■	59	

"And he arose, and rebuked the wind, and said unto the sea, Peace, be still. And the wind ceased, and there was a great calm." — Mark 4:39.

NUMBER 25

A LEGION OF DEMONS CAST OUT

HORIZONTAL

1 " . . . doctrine is not mine, but his that sent me" John 7:16
3 See 6 across
6 and 3 "What . . . thy . . . " Mark 5:9
10 "when he saw Jesus . . . off" Mark 5:6
12 Nickel
14 Golf mound
16 Steel helmet
19 "Now . . . was . . . nigh unto the mountains" Mark 5:11
21 Genuine
22 Grief
24 "that he would not . . . them away out of the country" Mark 5:10
25 "And he said, . . . : because many devils" Luke 8:30
28 Greek letter
29 Another Greek letter
31 "he . . . and worshipped him" Mark 5:6
33 Southern state
34 "pass over unto the other . . . " Mark 4:35
35 Iron
36 King of Bashan Josh. 13:12
37 "that thou torment . . . not" Mark 5:7
38 Dross of a metal
40 Topographical Engineer
41 " . . . he said unto him, Come out of the man" Mark 5:8
43 "that . . . may enter into them" Mark 5:12
44 Wine vessel of early Christian church
47 One of the disciples Matt. 4:18
49 Ladies
51 "and in his right . . . " Mark 5:15
53 Greek form of Noah
55 "Had been often bound . . . fetters and chains" Mark 5:4
56 "But so shall it not . . . among you" Mark 10:43
57 Blown by the wind
59 "Ye . . . the salt of the earth" Matt. 5:13
60 "an herd of . . . swine" Luke 8:32
61 "And he said unto them, . . . " Matt. 8:32
A saying of the demoniac is 1, 3, 6, 25, 41, 43, 59, and 60 combined

VERTICAL

2 The god of departed spirits (Hindu myth.)
3 Man's nickname
4 Capital of Moab Num. 21:28
5 Half an em
7 "down a . . . place into the sea" Mark 5:13
8 "a great herd of swine . . . " Mark 5:11
9 "and all men did . . . " Mark 5:20
11 "and . . . down before him" Luke 8:28
13 "and told . . . in the city, and in the country" Mark 5:14
15 Sea eagles
17 Second note in scale
18 "the whole herd of . . . ran violently" Matt. 8:32
20 Here lies (L.)
23 Small yellow bird
26 Son of Gad Gen. 46:16
27 "into the country of the . . .s" Mark 5:1
30 "neither could any man . . . him" Mark 5:4
32 "and were choked in the . . . " Mark 5:13
35 "And they that kept them . . . " Matt. 8:33
38 Compass point
39 Street urchin
40 "Who had his dwelling among the . . . " Mark 5:3
41 "And they that . . . the swine fled" Mark 5:14
42 Old Testament
45 "immediately there . . . him out of the tombs" Mark 5:2
46 "he planteth an . . . " Isa. 44:14
47 Promissory note
48 "there was no . . . for them in the inn" Luke 2:7
50 "suffer us to go . . . into the herd of swine" Matt. 8:31
52 Namely
54 Highest note in scale of Guido
57 Diphthong
58 "began to publish . . . Decapolis how great things" Mark 5:20

	1	2		3	4		5		6	7		8
9		10	11				12	13		14	15	
16	17					18		19	20			
21						22	23		24			
			25	26	27					28		
29	30			31					32			
33			34					35			36	
	37						38			39		
40			41	42			43			44	45	46
		47				48		49	50			
51	52				53		54		55			
56				57				58				
		59				60					61	

"Go home to thy friends, and tell them how great things the Lord hath done for thee, and hath had compassion on thee." — Mark 5:19.

NUMBER 26

THE SECOND REJECTION AT NAZARETH

HORIZONTAL

2 "And . . . went out from thence" Mark 6:1
4 "which have been since the world . . . " Luke 1:70
8 Dialect of Eastern Assam
10 "the thirteenth day of the twelfth month, which is the month . . . " Esth. 8:12
12 A city of Benjamin I Chron. 8:12
13 Assistant
15 "And he went . . . about the villages, teaching" Mark 6:6
16 "And when the . . . day was come" Mark 6:2
18 "is written with a . . . of iron" Jer. 17:1
19 Egyptian solar deity
20 "upon the great . . . of their right foot" Ex. 29:20
21 "and stood up for . . . read" Luke 4:16
22 "whosoever shall do and . . . them" Matt. 5:19
25 North River
26 and 53 "And he could there do . . . mighty . . . " Mark 6:5
28 "What . . . is this which is given unto him" Mark 6:2
29 Topographical Engineer
30 " . . . hath done what . . . could" Mark 14:8
31 "and sitting upon an . . . " Matt. 21:5
33 "and . . . mighty works" Matt. 13:54
36 Israelite of the tribe of Asher I Chron. 7:34
37 Egyptian sun god
38 "but . . . his own country" Mark 6:4
39 "And he closed . . . book" Luke 4:20
41 The (F. pl.)
42 One twelfth of a foot
44 Taxi
46 Doctor of Theology
47 "the brother . . . James, and Joses, and . . . Juda, and Simon" Mark 6:3
49 Snakelike fish
51 Meadow
53 See 26 across
56 "drowsiness shall clothe a man with . . .s" Prov. 23:21
58 "For this . . . is mount Sinai in Arabia" Gal. 4:25
59 "he taught them in their . . . " Matt. 13:54

Our text is 2, 4, 21, 22, 38, 39, and 59 combined

VERTICAL

1 "Is not this the . . . " Mark 6:3
2 "where David himself and his men were wont to . . . " I Sam. 30:31
3 Sea eagle
4 Buyer's option
5 "let him seek peace, and . . . it" I Pet. 3:11 (pl.)
6 The marsh crocodile
7 Hammer of a gun
8 "and many hearing him were . . . " Mark 6:2
9 "Let us pass over unto the . . . side" Mark 4:35
11 Female deer
14 "gave it again to the minister, and . . . down" Luke 4:20
17 Four fifths of bacon
19 Pens
23 "can . . . one cubit unto his stature" Matt. 6:27
24 His majesty
27 Whirlwind off the Faroe Islands
28 "From . . . hath this man these things" Mark 6:2
30 Part of leg between ankle and knee
31 Indian mulberry
32 "and are not his . . . here with us" Mark 6:3
34 And (F.)
35 "laid his hands upon a few sick folk, and . . .ed them" Mark 6:5
40 House of Commons
43 Grecian supreme goddess
45 Lover
47 "and among his . . . kin" Mark 6:4
48 Field Officer
50 Loiter
52 "he is of . . . ; ask him" John 9:21
54 Recording Secretary
55 Southern state
57 "that they may . . . into the country" Mark 6:36

1		2	3		4	5	6		7		8	9
10	11				12				13	14		
15						16		17				
18					19					20		
		21			22		23		24		25	
26	27			28								
29			30							31		32
		33				34		35		36		
37			38			39	40			41		
		42			43		44		45		46	
47	48			49		50		51		52		
53		54	55		56		57		58			
		59										

"A prophet is not without honour, save in his own country, and in his own house." — Matt. 13:57.

NUMBER 27

JESUS SENDS OUT THE TWELVE APOSTLES

HORIZONTAL

1 "is not . . . of me" Matt. 10:38
5 "And as ye go, . . . , saying" Matt. 10:7
10 "and brought him to an . . . " Luke 10:34
11 "cause them to be put to . . . " Matt. 10:21
12 Selenium
13 Cook in frying pan
15 "freely ye have received, freely . . . " Matt. 10:8
16 "a . . . of cold water" Matt. 10:42
18 Afternoon
19 Sounds
20 "but are not able to kill the . . . " Matt. 10:28
22 Canada West
23 Go back to the sign (music)
24 "shall receive . . . prophet's reward" Matt. 10:41
26 Wrath
27 Small yellow birds
29 "he that taketh not his . . . , and followeth" Matt. 10:38
31 "and . . . that receiveth me" Matt. 10:40
33 Himalayan panda
35 Plural ending of nouns; 12 turned around
36 "And . . . not them which kill the body" Matt. 10:28
38 Jesus the Saviour of Men (Latin initials)
40 "what ye hear in the . . . , that preach ye" Matt. 10:27
41 " . . . the lepers" Matt. 10:8
45 " . . . neither gold, nor silver" Matt. 10:9
47 "he planteth an . . . " Isa. 44:14
49 "He that findeth his life shall . . . it" Matt. 10:39
50 "deny me before men, him will I . . . deny" Matt. 10:33
51 "cast out first the beam out of thine own . . . " Luke 6:42
52 "take no thought how or what ye shall . . . " Matt. 10:19
53 "Why could not . . . cast him out" Mark 9:28

VERTICAL

1 " . . . as serpents" Matt. 10:16
2 "shall give to drink unto . . . of these little ones" Matt 10:42
3 Royal Navy
4 "The . . . truly is plenteous" Matt. 9:37
5 "I came not to send . . . , but a sword" Matt. 10:34
6 Sun god
7 And (F.)
8 "and said, . . . , . . . , our eye hath seen it" Ps. 35:21
9 "and . . . as doves" Matt. 10:16
13 "loseth his life for my sake shall . . . it" Matt. 10:39
14 Yea
15 "But . . . rather to the lost sheep" Matt. 10:6
17 Postscript
18 "nor brass in your . . . " Matt. 10:9
19 "Are not . . . sparrows sold for a farthing" Matt. 10:29
21 Hawaiian food fish
22 "Whosoever therefore shall . . . me before men" Matt. 10:32
25 Established Church
28 "Wherefore rebuke them . . . " Titus 1:13
30 Brazilian coins
32 Ancestor of Jesus Luke 3:28
33 "I send you forth as sheep in the midst of . . . " Matt. 10:16
34 "the very hairs of your . . . are all numbered" Matt. 10:30
37 Babylonian deity
39 " . . . the sick" Matt. 10:8
41 Cosine; companies
42 Two fifths of eight
43 New England
44 "neither two coats, neither . . .s, nor yet staves" Matt. 10:10
46 Deer
48 Compass point
50 Half akin

1	2	3		4			5	6	7	8		9
10						11						
12			13		14							
		15					16		17		18	
	19								20	21		
22			23			24		25		26		
27		28						29	30			
		31	32		33		34				35	
36	37								38	39		
40				41		42		43				44
		45	46							47	48	
		49							50			
	51				52						53	

"And they went out, and preached that men should repent." — Mark 6:12.

NUMBER 28

THE FEEDING OF THE FIVE THOUSAND

HORIZONTAL

1 "look up, and lift up your . . . " Luke 21:28
5 Third note in scale
7 "Shall we go and . . . two hundred pennyworth of bread" Mark 6:37
9 Home of Abram before he went to Canaan Gen. 11:28
10 Opus
11 "joy shall be in heaven . . . one sinner that repenteth" Luke 15:7
12 Babylonian deity
14 "And they took up . . . baskets full of the fragments" Mark 6:43
16 "when he had sent them . . . , he departed into a mountain to pray" Mark 6:46
18 Girl's name
19 Timid (Scot.)
20 "for he himself knew what he would . . . " John 6:6
21 "called the altar . . . " John 22:34
25 Doctor
27 "gave them to his disciples to . . . before them" Mark 6:41
28 "must suffer many things, and be set . . . nought" Mark 9:12
30 "And the people, when they knew . . . , followed him" Luke 9:11
32 Artificial language
34 "and the two . . . " Mark 6:41
38 River
39 Selenium
40 One of the prophets
41 Half an em
42 Force
43 "And he . . . them to make all sit down" Mark 6:39
46 Plural ending of nouns
47 "they were as . . . not having a shepherd" Mark 6:34
48 Daniel was cast into the . . . of lions

VERTICAL

1 "they sat down in ranks, by . . . , and by fifties" Mark 6:40
2 Ancestor of Jesus Luke 3:28
3 "and the disciples to them that were set . . . " John 6:11
4 "when the day was now far . . . " Mark 6:35
5 "was . . . with compassion" Mark 6:34
6 I have (cont.)
7 "and blessed, and . . . the loaves" Mark 6:41
8 "his parents went to Jerusalem every . . . " Luke 2:41
13 Yeas
14 Tantalum
15 Chinese measure
17 A little soft mass of some substance
22 "they say, Five, and . . . fishes" Mark 6:38
23 "go and . . . " Mark 6:38
24 "And they did all . . . , and were filled" Mark 6:42
26 Second note in scale
28 Head of a family of Gad I Chron. 5:15
29 "he began to . . . them many things" Mark 6:34
31 Travel on foot
32 "that they may go into the country . . . about" Mark 6:36
33 " . . . them away" Mark 6:36
34 " . . . loaves" Mark 6:41
35 Egyptian household goddess
36 Two books in the Old Testament
37 "over Edom will I cast out my . . . " Ps. 60:8
39 "do not your alms before men, to be . . . of them" Matt. 6:1
44 "and hast loved them, as thou hast loved . . . " John 17:23
45 Of

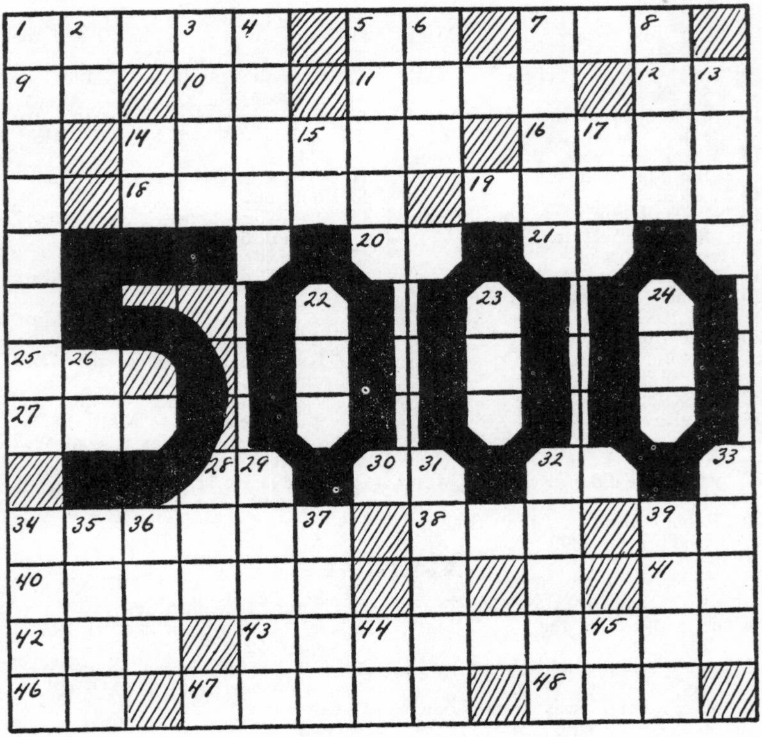

"He looked up to heaven, and blessed, and brake the loaves, and gave them to his disciples to set before them; and the two fishes divided he among them all." — Mark 6:41.

NUMBER 29

JESUS WALKS ON THE WATER

HORIZONTAL

1 "Then they that were . . . the ship came and worshipped him" Matt. 14:33
3 "Stand in . . . , and sin not" Ps. 4:4
5 "And he said, . . . " Matt. 14:29
10 "Be . . . good cheer" Matt. 14:27
12 "they supposed it had been . . . spirit" Mark 6:49
13 "I am the way, the . . . , and the life" John 14:6
14 Walked
16 "if it fall into a . . . on the sabbath day" Matt. 12:11
17 Japanese measure
18 Plane surface
19 "in the . . .th watch of the night" Matt. 14:25
20 More rare
21 Combining form signifying through
23 Greek letter
24 Weight
26 "and . . . down your nets for a draught" Luke 5:4
27 "wherefore didst . . . doubt" Matt. 14:31
30 "Rabbi, thou . . . the Son of God" John 1:49
31 "when he saw . . . wind boisterous" Matt. 14:30
32 Calcium
33 "saying, Lord, . . . me" Matt. 14:30
35 "ship was now in the . . . of the sea" Matt. 14:24
37 "and the archers . . . him" I Sam. 31:3
39 "when they were come into the ship, the wind . . . " Matt. 14:32
41 Servant of Solomon Ezra 2:57
43 Finds out
46 "that lie upon . . . of ivory" Amos 6:4
48 American Bible Society
49 "This is my beloved . . . " Matt. 3:17
50 "O thou . . . little faith" Matt. 14:31
52 "Thou shalt worship the Lord thy . . . " Luke 4:8
54 "saw him walking on the sea, they were . . . " Matt. 14:26
55 "for the . . . was contrary" Matt. 14:24

Our text is 10, 12, 13, 27, 30, 31, 49, 50, and 52 combined

VERTICAL

2 "be . . . afraid" Matt. 14:27
4 "he walked on the . . . " Matt. 14:29
5 "and beginning to sink, he . . . , saying" Matt. 14:30
6 "when Peter was come down . . . of the ship" Matt. 14:29
7 . . . of Olives
8 Exclamation of inquiry
9 "saying, It is a . . . " Matt. 14:26
11 "and they cried out for . . . " Matt. 14:26
13 Township
14 "immediately Jesus . . . forth his hand" Matt. 14:31
15 Prefix meaning before
17 East Indian coin (pl.)
19 Fourth note of scale
22 " . . . is I" Matt. 14:27
24 "tossed with . . .s" Matt. 14:24
25 "give unto you power to . . . on serpents and scorpions" Luke 10:19
26 Doctor of Humanities
28 City of Benjamin east of Bethel Gen. 12:8
29 "For he that is not against . . . is on our part" Mark 9:40
31 Current
34 Sour
35 "much people . . . him" Luke 9:37
36 The ship was . . . about on the sea
38 Prohibited
40 "Jesus went unto them, walking on the . . . " Matt. 14:25
42 Bill of fare
44 Moslem judge
45 Terbium
47 Sun
49 Senior
51 Iron
53 The beginning of owing

1	2	■	3	4		■	5	6	7	8	■	9
■	10	11	■	12	■	13					■	
14			15		■	16			■	■	17	
	■	18				■		■	19			
20					■	■	21	22		■	23	
	■	■	■	■	24	25	■		■	26		
27	28		29	■	30			■	31			■
32		■	33	34			■	35				36
37		38	■	39			40			■	■	
	■	41	42		■	43				44	45	
	■	46			47	■		■	■	48		
■	49			■	50	51	■	52	53		■	
54								■	55			

"And in the fourth watch of the night Jesus went unto them, walking on the sea." — Matt. 14:25.

NUMBER 30

THE SYROPHOENICIAN WOMAN ENTREATS JESUS TO HEAL HER DAUGHTER

HORIZONTAL

1 "Then came she and . . . him, saying" Matt. 15:25
10 Anglo-Saxon money
11 "took the little book out of the angel's hand, and . . . it up" Rev. 10:10
12 "O woman, great is thy . . . " Matt. 15:28
14 "Have . . . on me, O Lord" Matt. 15:22
16 Tuesday
17 Diphthong
18 An early period of time, a combining form
19 "and said unto him, . . . , Lord" Mark 7:28
22 Scoff
24 Girl's name
26 Summer (F.)
27 "saying, Lord, . . . me" Matt. 15:25
28 Solicitor-general
30 "and to . . . it to dogs" Matt. 15:26
33 Portico
35 "whose fingers and . . . were four and twenty" I Chron. 20:6
38 Awe-inspiring
41 See 63 across
43 "besought him that . . . would cast forth the devil" Mark 7:26
44 "which is gone down in the sun . . . of Ahaz" Isa. 38:8
46 Born
47 "But he answered her not a . . . " Matt. 15:23
49 Religious Tract Society
50 Doctor
51 Assimilated form signifying in or to
52 "on the sabbath loose his . . . or his ass from the stall" Luke 13:15
54 Western continent
56 Long gaiter
59 "And she said, . . . Lord" Matt. 15:27
62 "into the coasts of Tyre and . . . " Matt. 15:21
63 and 41 "It is not . . . to take the children's . . . " Matt. 15:26

VERTICAL

1 "a certain . . . , whose young daughter had an unclean spirit" Mark 7:25
2 Native metal
3 More rare
4 "if any man build upon this foundation gold, silver, precious stones, wood, . . . , stubble" I Cor. 3:12
5 and 47 "be . . . unto thee even as thou . . . " Matt. 15:28
6 Word before verse 129 of the 119th Psalm
7 Small lizard
8 "the devil is gone out of thy . . . " Mark 7:29
9 "am not sent but unto the lost . . . " Matt. 15:24
13 "which fall from their masters' . . . " Matt. 15:27
15 "woman of Canaan came out of the same . . . " Matt. 15:22
19 "And . . . are Christ's; and Christ is God's" I Cor. 3:23
20 And so forth
21 "The scribes and the Pharisees sit in Moses' . . . " Matt. 23:2
23 Namely
25 " . . . these two commandments hang all the law and the prophets" Matt. 22:40
29 "there is none . . . but one, that is, God" Matt. 19:17
31 Convulsive sigh
32 Laughter sound
33 "whom David and Samuel the . . . did ordain" I Chron. 9:22
34 Mohammedan ruler (var.)
36 " . . . her away" Matt. 15:23
37 Poem
39 "her daughter was made . . . from that very hour" Matt. 15:28
40 See 48 down
42 Combine with air
45 Linnaean Society
47 See 5 down
48 and 40 "yet the . . . . . . of the crumbs" Matt. 15:27
53 Chapter in Rev. beginning, "And there appeared a great wonder in heaven"
54 . . . Matthew
55 "to whom hath the . . . of the Lord been revealed" John 12:38
57 No date
58 " . . . ye therefore, and teach all nations" Matt. 28:19
60 In the midst of dues
61 By this title (L.)

1	2	3		4	5	6		7	8			9
10				11				12			13	
14			15					16			17	
		18			19	20	21		22	23		
24	25				26				27			
			28	29		30		31				
32		33			34		35			36		37
38	39					40		41			42	
	43			44			45			46		
47			48		49					50		
51			52	53				54	55			
56					57	58		59		60		61
			62						63			

"O woman, great is thy faith: be it unto thee even as thou wilt." — Matt. 15:28.

NUMBER 31

THE DISCIPLES CONFESS JESUS AS THE MESSIAH

HORIZONTAL

1 " . . . others, Jeremias" Matt. 16:14
4 "he hath founded it . . . the seas" Ps. 24:2
8 " . . . shall not be unto thee" Matt. 16:22
12 "which built his house upon a . . . " Matt. 7:24
13 A city of Benjamin I Chron. 8:12
14 Girl's name
15 Kine (Scot.)
17 and 18 "And . . . . . . give unto thee the keys of the kingdom" Matt. 16:19
20 "pull down my barns, and . . . greater" Luke 12:18
22 "but . . . Father which is in heaven" Matt. 16:17
23 "neglect to hear them, tell it unto the . . . " Matt. 18:17
25 Regius Professor
27 "But whom say . . . that I am" Matt. 16:15
28 Hebrew deity
29 At sea
31 " . . . I say also unto thee, That thou art Peter" Matt. 16:18
33 "Thou art . . . Christ" Matt. 16:16
35 "the stranger that is in thy . . . " Deut. 14:21
36 "the Son . . . the living God" Matt. 16:16
37 "and not that thy whole body should be cast into . . . " Matt. 5:29
38 River in Italy
39 "some, . . . " Matt. 16:14
41 Self (Scot.)
43 "bind on earth . . . be bound in heaven" Matt. 16:19
46 and 57 "flesh and blood hath . . . revealed . . . unto thee" Matt. 16:17
48 "Perceive ye how ye . . . nothing" John 12:19
50 Suffix forming participle
51 "and . . . I say, Rejoice" Phil. 4:4
52 Whirlwind off the Faroe Islands
53 Highest note in scale of Guido
55 Nova Scotia
56 "not with me is . . . me" Matt. 12:30
57 See 46 across
A saying of Jesus is 1, 4, 8, 12, 17, 18, 20, 22, 23, 31, 33, 35, 36, 37, 43, 46, 48, 56, and 57 combined

VERTICAL

1 Capital of Moab Num. 21:28
2 "Do ye . . . believe" John 16:31
3 District of Columbia
5 French infantryman
6 ". . . of the prophets" Matt. 16:14
7 "and your joy . . . man taketh from you" John 16:22
8 Thallium
9 "he hath sent me to . . . the brokenhearted" Luke 4:18
10 "shall be loosed . . . heaven" Matt. 16:19
11 "Whom do men . . . that I, the Son of man, am" Matt. 16:13
15 Knight of the Legion of Honor
16 What did you say?
17 I am (cont.)
19 "He casteth forth his . . . like morsels" Ps. 147:17
20 Bachelor of Civil Law
21 Tedious (Prov. Eng.)
24 "They . . . to and fro" Ps. 107:27
26 "And it came to . . . " Luke 9:18
27 Three feet
29 Lava
30 "We have seen . . . things today" Luke 5:26
31 Dialect of Eastern Assam
32 Newfoundland
33 Tellurium
34 House of Lords
35 Channels worn in the earth by water
37 " . . . , every one that thirsteth" Isa. 55:1
38 "between blood and blood, between . . . and . . . ," Deut. 17:8
39 Same as 28 across
40 "Let your light . . . shine before men" Matt. 5:16
41 "and meted out heaven with the . . . " Isa. 40:12
42 Unit of work (pl.)
43 Paul and Silas prayed, and . . . praises unto God" Acts 16:25
44 In the middle of this
45 Indian plant used for dyeing
47 "Some say . . . thou art John the Baptist" Matt. 16:14
49 By the way of
52 "whatsoever thou shalt loose . . . earth" Matt. 16:19
54 Long Island

1	2	3	■	4	5	6	7	■	8	9	10	11
12				■	13			■	14			
■		■	■	15			■	16	■		■	
17	■	18	19			■	20				21	■
22		■	23			24			■	■	25	26
■	■	27		■	■	28		■	29	30		
31	32		■	33	34		■	35				
36		■	37				■		■		■	
■	■	38		■	■	■	39				40	■
41	42		■	43	44	45			■	46		47
48			49				■	50			■	
51					■	■	52		■	53	54	
55		■	56							■	57	

"Thou art the Christ, the Son of the living God." — Matt. 16:16.

NUMBER 32

THE TRANSFIGURATION

HORIZONTAL

1 " . . . bringeth them up into an high mountain apart" Matt. 17:1
3 "they saw . . . glory" Luke 9:32
6 "steadfastly set his . . . to go to Jerusalem" Luke 9:51
9 Artificial language
10 Cab
11 "The lot is cast into the . . . " Prov. 16:33
13 "the works which none other man . . . " John 15:24
14 "Let your light so . . . before men" Matt. 5:16
16 "This is my beloved . . . " Matt. 17:5
17 "If my . . . hath turned out of the way" Job 31:7
18 Data
19 "they feared . . . they entered into the cloud" Luke 9:34
20 "when . . . voice was past" Luke 9:36
21 "his countenance was as the . . . shineth in his strength" Rev. 1:16
22 The disciples were full of . . .
23 "wherein shall go no galley with . . . " Isa. 33:21
25 Of
26 "one for thee, . . . one for Moses, . . . one for Elias" Matt. 17:4
27 "Jesus taketh Peter, James, and John . . . brother" Matt. 17:1
30 "called the altar . . . " Josh. 22:34
31 " . . . us make here three tabernacles" Matt. 17:4
33 "Jesus was found a . . . " Luke 9:36
34 "his . . . became shining" Mark 9:3
35 Ancestor of Jesus Luke 3:28
37 Become weary
39 "in whom I am well pleased: . . . ye him" Matt. 17:5
41 "there . . . a cloud that overshadowed them" Mark 9:7
42 "raiment was . . . and glistering" Luke 9:29
46 "exceeding white . . . snow" Mark 9:3
47 Bone
48 "and fashioned it with a graving . . . " Ex. 32:4
49 Flowers
52 "there came a voice out of . . . cloud" Luke 9:35
53 "The people which sat in darkness saw great . . . " Matt. 4:16

Our text is 1, 3, 6, 13, 14, 19, 20, 21, 26, 27, 34, 41, 42, 46, 52, and 53 combined

VERTICAL

1 Shewed strength with his . . . " Luke 1:51
2 "and told . . . man" Luke 9:36
3 "If I . . . not come" John 15:22
4 Number of "Transfiguration" chapters in Mark and Luke
5 "The same is my brother, and my . . . , and mother" Mark 3:35
6 Tosses up
7 "all things are . . . unto you" Luke 11:41
8 Babylonian deity
10 "brass, and . . . , and iron, and lead" Ezek. 22:18
12 "And as he . . . ," Luke 9:29
13 Give medicine to
15 "and . . . was transfigured" Mark 9:2
16 "they . . . no man," Matt. 17:8
17 Fish
20 Two-wheeled cart used in India
22 "Come unto me, . . . ye that labour" Matt. 11:28
24 "put off thy . . . from thy foot" Isa. 20:2
25 "and spake of his . . . which he should accomplish" Luke 9:31
28 "no room for them in the . . . " Luke 2:7
29 Son of Adam and Eve Gen. 4:25
32 "there appeared unto them Moses and . . . talking with him" Matt. 17:3
33 Long meter
34 Second note in scale
36 Means of travel
37 "With him . . . men" Luke 9:30 (pl.)
38 Recording Secretary
40 "His star in the . . . " Matt. 2:2
42 "But . . . unto you, scribes," Matt. 23:13
43 " . . . , every one that thirsteth" Isa. 55:1
44 "Love worketh no . . ." Rom. 13:10
45 Unit of work
48 Thursday; thorium
50 Exclamation
51 " . . . as no fuller on earth can white them" Mark 9:3

1	2		■	3	4	5	■	6		7	8	■
9		■	10				■		■	11		12
	■	13			■	14	15				■	
■	16			■	17				■	18		
■	19		■	20			■	21			■	
22			■	23			24	■	■	■	25	
	■	■	26			■	27	28	29	■	30	
31	32		■		■	33				■		■
■		■	34							■	35	36
37		38		■	■	■	■	■	39	40		
41			■	42	43	44		45	■	46		■
47		■	48				■	49	50			51
	■	52			■	53					■	

"And behold a voice out of the cloud, which said, This is my beloved Son, in whom I am well pleased; hear ye him." — Matt. 17:5.

NUMBER 33

JESUS SHOWS THE DISCIPLES WHO IS GREATEST IN THE KINGDOM OF HEAVEN

HORIZONTAL

1 Finale of a musical composition (pl.)
5 "Whosoever shall receice this child in my name receiveth . . . " Luke 9:48
6 and 11 " . . . was it . . . ye disputed" Mark 9:33
9 " . . . by the way they had disputed" Mark 9:34
10 "And . . . took a child" Mark 9:36
11 See 6 across
12 Grand Tyler
13 "and went forth to . . . him" John 12:13
14 "if the salt have lost his saltness, wherewith will ye season . . . " Mark 9:50
16 "the same . . . greatest" Matt. 18:4
17 "done it unto one of the . . . of these my brethren" Matt. 25:40
20 "not say in their hearts, . . . , so would we have it" Ps. 35:25
21 Printer's measure (pl.)
23 Natural force
24 Leaves
26 "disputed . . . themselves" Mark 9:34
28 "He that heareth . . ." Luke 10:16
29 "and servant of . . ." Mark 9:35
31 Topographical Engineer
32 "shall not be taken away from . . . " Luke 10:42
33 City or town in South Africa
34 "called . . . twelve" Mark 9:35
36 and 30 down "the . . . shall be . . . of all" Mark 9:35
38 Senior
39 "Let your light . . . shine" Matt. 5:16
40 Right Guard
42 Egg-shaped
43 "Whosoever . . . receive one of such children" Mark 9:37
45 "If any man desire to . . . first" Mark 9:35
46 Whirlwinds off the Faroe Islands
48 "many knew him, and . . . afoot thither" Mark 6:33
51 Girl's name
52 "whosoever will be . . . among you, shall be your minister" Mark 10:43
55 Cloth broom for scrubbing
57 "and . . . him in the midst of them" Mark 9:36
58 "Then there arose a . . . among them" Luke 9:46

A saying of Jesus is 9, 10, 11, 16, 17, 26, 28, 29, 34, 36, 43, 45, and 52 combined

VERTICAL

2 "how . . . shall my brother sin against me" Matt. 18:21
3 "What shall we . . . , "John 6:28
4 "and when he had taken him in his . . . , he said" Mark 9:36
5 "With what measure ye . . . , it shall be measured to you" Mark 4:24
6 "his raiment was . . ." Luke 9:29
7 Head covering
8 "he was sad . . . that saying" Mark 10:22
10 "But they . . . their peace" Mark 9:34
12 "Who is the . . . " Matt. 18:1
15 "and become as little . . . " Matt. 18:3
16 Combining form signifying equality
18 Public square of an ancient Greek city
19 French copper coin
22 Madame
23 King of Bashan Num. 21:33
25 "And he . . . down" Mark 9:35
27 Nahum
28 Yea
30 See 36 across
33 "and . . . the wicked" Matt. 13:49
35 Age
37 Crowd
41 A bright dazzling light
43 "receiveth him that . . . me" Luke 9:48
44 Here lies (L.)
46 "whoso shall receive . . . such little child" Matt. 18:5
47 when he . . . gone forth" Mark 10:17
49 Servant of Solomon Ezra 2:57
50 Not
51 "love thy neighbour . . . thyself" Matt. 19:19
52 Grain
53 Babylonian deity
54 "Suffer the little children . . . come unto me" Mark 10:14
56 Portuguese

1	2	3	4			5			6	7	8	
	9				10			11				
12			13						14			15
		16			17		18	19			20	
21	22			23			24			25		
26			27			28				29	30	
31					32				33			
		34		35		36		37			38	
39				40	41			42				
		43	44					45				
	46						47		48	49	50	
51				52		53		54		55		56
57				58								

"At the same time came the disciples unto Jesus, saying, Who is the greatest in the kingdom of heaven?" — Matt. 18:1.

NUMBER 34

THE TEACHING OF JESUS ABOUT FORGIVENESS AND THE PARABLE OF THE WICKED SERVANT

HORIZONTAL

1 "saying, Pay me that thou . . . " Matt. 18:28
5 "till he should pay the . . . " Matt. 18:30
9 Lord Provost
11 "they put the branch to their . . . " Ezek. 8:17
12 "which owed him an hundred . . . " Matt. 18:28
13 "in the mouth of two . . . three witnesses" Matt. 18:16
14 Ancestor of Jesus Luke 3:28
15 Greek letter
16 "Blessed are the eyes which . . . the things that ye . . . " Luke 10:23
18 "if thy brother shall . . . against thee" Matt. 18:15
23 "And . . . he had begun to reckon" Matt. 18:24
24 Stray
25 "Give us of your . . . ; for our lamps are gone out" Matt. 25:8
26 Compass point
27 "any thing that they shall ask, . . . shall be done" Matt. 18:19
28 Manganese
29 Regius Professor
31 Equality, a combining form
33 Doctor of Philosophy
34 "his Lord commanded him . . . be sold" Matt. 18:25
36 "his fellowservant fell down at his . . . " Matt. 18:29
37 "what ye hear in the . . . , that preach ye" Matt. 10:27
39 "that they may be one, as . . . are" John 17: 11
40 Messenger
42 "as a . . . lappeth" Judg. 7:5
43 Sores
46 Two-surfaced glass
47 "the lord of that . . . was moved with compassion" Matt. 18:27
52 "if two of you shall . . . on earth" Matt. 18:19
53 "when his fellow servants . . . what was done" Matt. 18:31
54 Yonder

VERTICAL

1 "then take with thee . . . or two more" Matt. 18:16
2 "servant therefore fell down, and . . . him" Matt. 18:26
3 Plural ending of nouns
4 "and I forgive him? till . . . times" Matt. 18:21
5 Of
6 Half an em
7 Before Christ
8 Tellurium
9 "those I counted . . . for Christ" Phil. 3:7
10 "cast him into . . . " Matt. 18:30
15 "forasmuch as he had not to . . . " Matt. 18:25
17 Snakelike fish
18 "which owed him . . . thousand talents" Matt. 18:24
19 Royal Society of Edinburgh
20 And (F.)
21 Holy Roman Empire (L.)
22 "Lord, have . . . with me, and I will pay thee all" Matt. 18:26
23 "every . . . may be established" Matt. 18:16
28 Engines
30 "and . . . him the debt" Matt. 18:27
32 "Until . . . times seven" Matt. 18:22
34 "where . . . or three are gathered together in my name" Matt. 18:20
35 Whirlwind off the Faroe Islands
36 "found one of his . . . servants" Matt. 18:28
38 Dialect of Eastern Assam
41 This (contr.)
44 A good king of Judah II Chron. 14:2
45 Pronoun
48 For example
49 Means of travel
50 Diphthong
51 "there am I . . . the midst of them" Matt. 18:20

"Then came Peter to him, and said, Lord, how oft shall my brother sin against me, and I forgive him? till seven times?" — Matt. 18:21.

NUMBER 35

JESUS HEALS THE MAN BORN BLIND

HORIZONTAL

2 "they called . . . parents of him" John 9:18
5 "all . . . in prayer to God" Luke 6:12
10 Genus of insects
12 "I was blind, now I . . . " John 9:25
13 North River
14 The letter C
16 Lava
17 "but he said, ... he" John 9:9 (two words)
18 "And it was the sabbath . . . " John 9:14
19 "Ye do . . . , not knowing the scriptures" Matt. 22:29
20 Two sevenths of Finland
21 "whom the lord when he . . . shall find watching" Luke 12:37
23 Compass point
25 "and I will give you . . . " Matt. 11:28
26 "Thou . . . both seen him" John 9:37
29 "(which is by interpretation, . . .)" John 9:7
31 Eagle's nest
32 "He that hath . . . to hear, let him hear" Luke 14:35
35 "that he was born . . . " John 9:2
36 " . . . he had thus spoken" John 9:6
38 "Whether he be a sinner or . . . , I know not" John 9:25
40 "A . . . that is called Jesus made clay" John 9:11
41 "Is not this he that . . . and begged" John 9:8
42 "What did he . . . thee" John 9:26
44 Fourth note in scale
46 Dry
48 Postscript
50 New Jersey
52 South Africa
54 Deputy Lieutenant
55 "Then said I, . . . ," Jer. 4:10
56 "for the Jews had a. . . already" John 9:22
59 . . . John
60 "How . . . a man that is a sinner do such miracles" John 9:16
61 "I must . . . the works of him that sent me" John 9:4
62 Yea
A saying of Jesus is 2, 5, 21, 36, 38, 40, 60, and 61 combined

VERTICAL

1 "that the works of God should be made . . . in him" John 9:3
2 One of the disciples; thorium
3 "Thou art . . . disciple" John 9:28
4 Plural ending of nouns
6 Grand Secretary
7 "I have told you already, and ye did not . . . " John 9:27
8 "the wild beast shall . . . them" Hosea 13:8
9 "and he . . . the eyes" John 9:6
11 "Give God the . . . " John 9:24
14 "and . . . seeing" John 9:7
15 "that he hath opened thine . . . " John 9:17
18 Ancient royal city of the Canaanites Josh. 11:2
19 Exclamation of inquiry
22 Size of shot
24 Half an em
26 "turned about with a very small . . . " Jas. 3:4
27 Tunes
28 "Neither hath this man . . . , nor his parents" John 9:3
30 Golf mound
31 Month in Hebrew calendar
33 "Go to the . . . ," Prov. 6:6
34 Tin
36 "Go, . . . in the pool of Siloam" John 9:7
37 Under this title (L.)
39 "If this man were not . . . God, he could do nothing" John 9:33
41 "he . . . on the ground" John 9:6
43 " . . . think I know" John 9:25
45 " . . . long . . . I am in the world, I am the light" John 9:5
47 "and made . . . of the spittle" John 9:6
49 Turkish commander
51 "because they feared the . . .s" John 9:22
53 "he is of age; . . . him" John 9:21
57 Royal Navy
58 "and I washed, and . . . see" John 9:15

1		2	3	4		5		6	7	8		9
10	11							12				
13					14	15			16			
17				18				19				
20			21				22					
23		24		25					26	27	28	
29			30					31				
			32	33		34		35				
	36	37				38	39		40			
41				42	43		44	45		46		47
48			49		50	51		52	53		54	
55			56	57			58		59			
		60				61					62	

"One thing I know, that, whereas I was blind, now I see." — John 9:25.

NUMBER 36

THE PARABLE OF THE GOOD SHEPHERD

HORIZONTAL

1 ". . . have power to lay it down" John 10:18
2 "I . . . come that they might have life" John 10:10
3 "for they know not . . . voice of strangers" John 10:5
5 "even . . . know I the Father" John 10:15
7 "because he . . . an hireling" John 10:13
8 South American monkey
9 "but I lay . . . down of myself" John 10:18
10 "what . . . thing shall I do, that I may have eternal life" Matt. 19:16
11 "one fold, and one . . ." John 10:16
14 Old Testament
15 Women's Christian Association
16 Father
17 Dialect of Eastern Assam
18 "To him . . . porter openeth" John 10:3
20 "there is none . . . but one, that is, God" Matt. 19:17
22 and 51 down ". . . man taketh it from . . ." John 10:18
23 "Blessed are the poor in spirit: for . . . is the kingdom of heaven" Matt. 5:3
25 Grain
26 "But he that entereth in by the door is the . . . of the sheep" John 10:2
28 . . . John
29 Western continent
30 "Thou . . . the Christ, the Son of the living God" Matt. 16:16
32 Tellurium
33 "my Father . . . you the true bread from heaven" John 6:32
36 "they shall . . . my voice" John 10:16
38 A Benjamite I Chron. 7:12
39 "Therefore doth my Father . . . me" John 10:17
41 "and he calleth . . . own sheep by name" John 10:3
43 "because I lay down my . . ." John 10:17
46 I am (cont.)
47 Smoothed
50 Froths
52 ". . . they know his voice" John 10:4
53 "and . . . wolf catcheth them" John 10:12
54 "and the . . . follow him" John 10:4
A saying of Jesus is 1, 2, 3, 10, 11, 18, 20, 26, 33, 41, 43, 52, 53, and 54 combined

VERTICAL

2 ". . . the Father knoweth me" John 10:15
3 Toe (Scot.)
4 Short for hippopotamus
5 "And a . . . will they not follow" John 10:5
6 "whose own the sheep are . . ." John 10:12
7 The same (L.)
8 Rough nap
9 Namely
10 "he . . . before them" John 10:4
11 South Carolina
12 Son of Ishmael, and grandson of Abraham I Chron. 1:30
13 "I am the . . . of the sheep" John 10:7
15 "understood not what things they . . . which he spake" John 10:6
18 Trial
19 His Imperial Highness
21 "Pay me that thou . . ." Matt. 18:28
24 Country in Europe
27 Hurrah
28 ". . .th the wolf coming" John 10:12
30 "Why make ye this . . . , and weep" Mark 5:39
31 ". . . also I must bring" John 10:16
32 "The . . . cometh not, but for to steal, and to kill, and to destroy" John 10:10
33 Broad smile
34 Number of chapter in Matthew beginning "Take heed that ye do not your alms before men"
35 . . .king (Scandinavian and German poetical mythology)
37 Another Benjamite I Chron. 7:12
39 Jacob's first wife Gen. 29:16–25
40 Device for holding objects
42 "A city that is . . . on an hill cannot be hid" Matt. 5:14
44 "by me . . . any man enter in, he shall be saved" John 10:9
45 Field Officers
48 Left-hand page (L.)
49 Deadhead
51 See 22 across

■	■	1	■	2		■	3	4		■	5	
■	6	■	7		■	8			■	9		■
10				■	11				12			13
14		■	■	15			■	16		■	17	
	■	18	19		■	20	21			■	22	
23					24	■		■		■	25	
	■	26						27		■		■
■	28		■	■	■	■	29		■	30		31
32		■	33		34	35			■		■	
36		37		■	38		■	■	39		40	
	■	41		42	■	43	44	45		■	46	
47	48				49	■	50			51		■
52			■	53			■	54				

"I am come that they might have life, and that they might have it more abundantly." — John 10:10.

NUMBER 37

JESUS SENDS FORTH THE SEVENTY

HORIZONTAL

1 "sent them . . . and . . . before his face" Luke 10:1
3 "he that . . . you despiseth me" Luke 10:16
10 Dialect of Eastern Assam
11 "go your ways . . . into the streets" Luke 10:10
12 Fervent (var.)
13 "nothing shall by any . . . hurt you" Luke 10:19
15 "shalt be thrust . . . to hell" Luke 10:15
17 Babylonian deity
18 "the seventy . . . again with joy" Luke 10:17
20 Capital of Moab Num. 21:28
21 "it shall be as the chased . . . " Isa. 13:14
22 Poem
24 "Peace . . . to this house" Luke 10:5
26 Notary Public
27 Be quiet
29 Plural ending of nouns
31 East Indies
32 Royal Highness
33 Father (F.)
36 "called the altar . . . " Josh. 22:34
37 Summers (F.)
38 "no man knoweth who the . . . is, but the Father" Luke 10:22
40 Here (F.)
43 "because your names are . . . in heaven" Luke 10:20
46 "I . . . thee, O Father" Luke 10:21
48 "for . . . it seemed good in thy sight" Luke 10:21
49 "sitting . . . sackcloth and ashes" Luke 10:13
50 High priest and judge of Israel I Sam. 3:1
51 Silkworm
53 "none is good, . . . one, that is, God" Luke 18:19
55 "the kingdom of God is come . . . unto you" Luke 10:11
56 "and who the . . . is, but the Son" Luke 10:22

VERTICAL

1 "But the tongue can no man . . ." Jas. 3:8
2 ". . . unto thee, Chorazin" Luke 10:13
3 "Even the very . . . of your city" Luke 10:11
4 And (F.)
5 Inclined
6 "I . . . you forth as lambs among wolves" Luke 10:3
7 For example
8 "give unto you power to . . . on serpents" Luke 10:19
9 "He that . . . you heareth me" Luke 10:16
11 "But . . . thing is needful" Luke 10:42
14 Same as 20 across
15 "and thy paths . . . fatness" Ps. 65:11
16 "Why could not . . . cast him out" Mark 9:28
19 Vases
23 "they had a great while ago . . . " Luke 10:13
25 "Blessed are the . . . which see" Luke 10:23
27 "many prophets and kings have desired to . . . those things" Luke 10:24
28 "that thou hast . . . these things from the wise and prudent" Luke 10:21
30 "eat such things as are . . . before you" Luke 10:8
32 "whatsoever city ye enter, and they . . . you" Luke 10:8
34 "And in the same house . . . " Luke 10:7
35 "and over all the . . . of the enemy" Luke 10:19
39 North River
40 "But . . . shall be more tolerable for Tyre and Sidon" Luke 10:14
44 "the labourer . . . worthy of his Acts 16:24
42 Correct
44 "the labourer . . . worthy of his hire" Luke 10:7
45 Tumbled about (var.)
47 House of Lords
51 Exclamation of inquiry
52 "And . . . the son of peace be there" Luke 10:6
54 "Then said I, . . . , Lord God" Jer. 4:10

1	2			3	4		5		6	7	8	9
10			11						12			
13		14				15		16			17	
		18			19						20	
					21					22		
23		24	25		26			27	28			
29	30							31			32	
33		34				35		36				
37					38		39			40		41
				42		43		44	45			
46	47							48			49	
50					51		52		53	54		
		55					56					

"Pray ye therefore the Lord of the harvest, that he would send forth labourers into his harvest." — Luke 10:2.

NUMBER 38

THE PARABLE OF THE GOOD SAMARITAN

HORIZONTAL

1 "Good . . . what shall I do that I may inherit eternal life" Mark 10:17
6 and 24 down " . . . is written in the . . . " Luke 10:26
9 "he . . . by on the other side" Luke 10:31
10 Chinese measure
11 "many knew him, and . . . afoot thither" Mark 6:33
13 Weary
14 "he took out two . . ." Luke 10:35
15 Compass point
17 "and . . . them to the host" Luke 10:35
18 Seventh note in scale
19 "in due season we . . . reap, if we faint not" Gal. 6:9
22 ". . . am crucified with Christ" Gal. 2:20
23 "this . . . , and thou shalt live" Luke 10:28
25 "by chance there came down a certain . . . that way" Luke 10:31
27 Royal Highness
28 "brought him to . . . inn" Luke 10:34
29 Daughter of one's brother or sister
31 Month in Hebrew calendar
34 ". . . , and do thou likewise" Luke 10:37
35 "man went down from Jerusalem . . . Jericho" Luke 10:30
36 ". . . the kingdom prepared for you" Matt. 25:34
40 "But a certain . . . , as he journeyed, came where he was" Luke 10:33
41 "Do ye not therefore . . . , because ye know not the Scriptures" Mark 12:24
43 "He casteth forth his . . . like morsels" Ps. 147:17
44 Sunday
45 Didymium
46 "Thou hast answered . . . " Luke 10:28
49 "and whatsoever thou spendest . . . " Luke 10:35
51 "Search the scriptures; for in them ye think ye have . . . life" John 5:39
52 "and shall inherit everlasting . . . " Matt. 19:29

Our text is 1, 6, 19, 22, 23, 35, 36, 51, and 52 combined

VERTICAL

1 Female horses
2 "If ye shall . . . anything in my name" John 14:14
3 Sunday School
4 "he called his . . . servants, and delivered them . . . pounds" Luke 19:13
5 "called the altar . . . " Josh. 22:34
6 "pouring in oil and . . . " Luke 10:34
7 "Ye . . . the light of the world" Matt. 5:14
8 Tantalum
9 "or will men take a . . . of it to hang any vessel thereon" Ezek. 15:3
10 "And likewise a . . . , when he was at the place" Luke 10:32
12 "And who is my . . . " Luke 10:29
14 Father
16 "and took . . . of him" Luke 10:34
17 Dale
20 High Priest
21 Same as 10 across
23 "but if it . . . , it bringeth forth much fruit" John 12:24
24 See 6 across
26 "for so it seemed good in thy . . . " Luke 10:21
27 "all our righteousnesses are as filthy . . .s" Isa. 64:6
30 A hornlike part
32 "when I . . . again, I will repay thee" Luke 10:35
33 "Then all those . . .s arose, and trimmed their lamps" Matt. 25:7
35 Silent
37 Nickel
38 "for we have seen his star in the . . . " Matt. 2:2
39 Tellurium
40 "and passed by on the other . . ." Luke 10:32
42 "And it is a . . . thing that the king requireth" Dan. 2:11
46 Means of travel
47 Southern state
48 House of Lords
49 Third note in scale
50 "stripped him . . . his raiment" Luke 10:30

	1	2	3	4	5			6		7	8	
9							10			11		12
13						14						
15			16		17						18	
	19	20		21			22		23			
24		25				26					27	
28					29			30			31	
		32		33							34	
	35			36	37		38			39		
40										41	42	
43							44					
45			46		47	48			49	50		
51								52				

"Thou shalt love the Lord thy God with all thy heart, and with all thy soul, and with all thy strength, and with all thy mind; and thy neighbour as thyself." — Luke 10:27.

NUMBER 39

THE RAISING OF LAZARUS FROM THE DEAD

HORIZONTAL

1 "Now Jesus loved Martha, . . . her sister, . . . Lazarus" John 11:5
3 "And blessed is he, . . . shall not be offended in me" Matt. 11:6
10 "And when she had . . . said, she went her way" John 11:28
11 "The Master is come, and . . . for thee" John 11:28
12 Automobile
13 "My head with . . . thou didst not anoint" Luke 7:46
15 "Go thy way; thy son . . . " John 4:50
18 "she arose quickly, . . . came unto him" John 11:29
20 "God will . . . it thee" John 11:22
21 Snakelike fish
23 Eye (Scot.)
24 Lord Provost
26 "Thrice was I beaten with . . . " II Cor. 11:25
28 Father
29 "he that . . . in me, though he were dead, yet shall he live" John 11:25
31 "saw the fig tree dried up from the . . . " Mark 11:20
32 Babylonian deity
33 Twelfth Greek letter
34 Second note in scale
35 Sister of Lazarus
38 "he found that he had lain . . . the grave four days" John 11:17
39 "I thank thee that thou hast heard . . . " John 11:41
40 "I know that he . . . rise again in the resurrection" John 11:24
42 Capital of Moab Num. 21:28
43 " . . . such things as are set before you" Luke 10:8 (pl.)
45 "And said, Where have ye . . . him" John 11:34
47 Another sister of Lazarus
49 "Thy brother shall . . . again" John 11:23
51 Beverage
52 "whosoever drinketh of the water that I shall give him shall . . . thirst" John 4:14
53 "Let us also go, that we may . . . with him" John 11:16

A saying of Jesus is 1, 3, 15, 18, 29, 38, 39, 40, 52, and 53 combined

VERTICAL

1 "even now, whatsoever thou wilt . . . of God" John 11:22
2 "and . . . man could bind him" Mark 5:3
3 "They were . . . of it, and fled unto Lystra and Derbe" Acts 14:6
4 House of Lords
5 In chemistry, a suffix denoting alcohols
6 "if thou wouldest believe, thou shouldest . . . the glory of God" John 11:40
7 Old Testament
8 Exclamation of inquiry
9 A son of Gad Gen. 46:16
11 "It was a . . . , and a stone lay upon it" John 11:38
12 Number of Psalm beginning, "Bless the Lord, O my soul. O Lord my God, thou art very great"
13 Poem
14 Jesus raised . . . from the dead
15 "The . . . of truth shall be established for ever" Prov. 12:19
16 Tellurium
17 "Lord, if thou hadst been . . . , my brother had not died" John 11:21
19 "and the swallow a . . . for herself" Ps. 84:3
20 "but for the . . . of God" John 11:4
22 ". . . of pleasures more than . . . of God" II Tim. 3:4
25 Indian plant used for dyeing (pl.)
27 "This sickness is not unto . . . " John 11:4
29 "Except a man be . . . again, he cannot see the kingdom of God" John 3:3
30 Summer (F.)
35 Unit of length in metric system
36 Man's name
37 Winged
38 One of David's guards I Chron. 11:40
39 Mother
41 "and whosoever loveth and maketh a . . . " Rev. 22:15
42 Servant of Solomon Ezra 2:57
43 "The light of the body is the . . . " Matt. 6:22
44 ". . . , I perceive that thou art a prophet" John 4:19
46 "If any man walk in the . . . , he stumbleth not" John 11:9
48 Royal Navy
50 "called the altar . . . " Josh. 22:34

1	2		■	3	4	5	6	7	8		9	
10		■	11							■		■
	■	12			■	■		■	■	13		14
■	15				16	17	■	18	19		■	
20				■	21		22	■	23		■	
24		■	■	25	■	26		27		■	28	
	■	29	30								■	
31					■	■	32		■	■	33	
	■	34		■	35				36	37	■	
■	38		■	39		■	40				41	■
42		■	43			44	■	■	45			46
47		48		■	49			50	■	51		
	■	52					■	53			■	

"Jesus said unto her, I am the resurrection, and the life: he that believeth in me, though he were dead, yet shall he live." — John 11:25.

NUMBER 40

THE HEALING OF THE TEN LEPERS

HORIZONTAL

1 and 31 "as they went, they . . . . . . " Luke 17:14
4 ". . . are not found that returned" Luke 17:18
8 "and they were . . . amazed" Mark 6:51
9 Recently extinct bird of New Zealand
10 "trespass against thee seven times . . . a day" Luke 17:4
12 and 4 down " . . . glory . . . God" Luke 17:18
14 ". . . hath done what . . . could" Mark 14:8
16 Father
17 Small yellow bird
19 "go . . . after them, nor follow them" Luke 17:23
20 There were . . . lepers cleansed
21 Royal Marines
22 See 8 down
25 By the way of
26 Joint connecting foot and leg (var.)
29 "men that were . . .s" Luke 17:12
31 See 1 across
32 Seventh note in scale
33 . . . returned to give thanks
35 ". . . not down in the highest room" Luke 14:8
36 Drops (medicine L.)
37 "Arise, . . . thy way" Luke 17:19
40 Table-land
41 ". . . first must he suffer many things" Luke 17:25
43 "that . . . I am, there ye may be also" John 14:3
45 "as he entered into a certain . . ." Luke 17:12
47 Pertaining to air, a combining form
48 Japanese measure
49 "with a . . . voice glorified God" Luke 17:15
51 "Blessed . . . the pure in heart" Matt. 5:8
52 ". . . kingdom of God is within you" Luke 17:21
53 "and . . . parts to dwell in other cities" Neh. 11:1
A saying of Jesus is 1, 4, 19, 20, 31, 41, 43, 51, 52, and 53 combined

VERTICAL

1 Grief
2 Unit of work
3 Strap of a bridle
4 See 12 across
5 "go and sell that thou . . ." Matt. 19:21
6 Nothing (F.)
7 Half an em
8 and 22 across "which . . . afar . . . " Luke 17:12
9 "there . . . him ten men" Luke 17:12
11 "and he was a . . . " Luke 17:16
13 "And they lifted up their . . . , and said" Luke 17:13
15 "when he saw that he was . . . " Luke 17:15
16 "Go shew yourselves unto the . . . " Luke 17:14
18 "passed through the midst . . . Samaria and Galilee" Luke 17:11
23 "And fell down on his . . . at his feet" Luke 17:16
24 "as he . . . to Jerusalem" Luke 17:11
25 Vice President
27 North latitude
28 "And now also the axe is . . . unto the root of the trees" Luke 3:9
30 Man's name
33 King of Bashan Josh. 13:12
34 "I find . . . fault in this man" Luke 23:4
36 To turn to the side away from the driver
38 "come a Governor, that shall . . . my people Israel" Matt. 2:6
39 " . . . sinful nation" Isa. 1:4
40 Title prefixed to names of men
41 Dark blue or bluish-gray color (Scot.)
42 Acid
43 Same as 1 across
44 Ancestor of Jesus Luke 3:28
45 Same as 25 across
46 "for ye tithe mint and . . . and all manner of herbs" Luke 11:42
49 Chinese measure
50 "Jesus, Master, have mercy . . . us" Luke 17:13

■	1	2	3		■	4	5		6	7	■	■
8				■	9			■	10		■	11
	■	12		13		■	14	15		■	16	
17	18	■	19			■	20			■	21	
22		23	■		■	24	■		■	25		
	■	26	27		28		■	29	30			
■	■	31								■	32	
33	34		■	35			■		■	36		
37		■	38	■		■	39	■	40			
■	■	41		42	■	43		44			■	
45							■		■	■	46	■
	■	47			■	48		■	49	50		
51			■	52			■	53				■

"And he said unto him, Arise, go thy way: thy faith hath made thee whole." — Luke 17:19.

NUMBER 41

THE PARABLE OF THE PRODIGAL SON

HORIZONTAL

1 "his father saw him, and had . . . " Luke 15:20
9 "I will arise and . . . to my father" Luke 15:18
10 "He saith among the trumpets, ... " Job 39:25
11 "give me the portion of . . . that falleth to me" Luke 15:12
12 See 45 across
15 "younger son gathered . . . together" Luke 15:13
16 Deadhead
17 "the younger . . . them said to his father" Luke 15:12
19 Convulsive sigh
22 Medley
24 "But when he was yet a great . . . off" Luke 15:20
26 Equal value
27 "and no man . . . unto him" Luke 15:16
28 Second note in scale
29 "Sir, come down . . . my child die" John 4:49
30 Nickel
33 Doctor of Divinity
34 ". . . that day ye shall ask in my name" John 16:26
36 Very small boy (colloq.)
37 "sent him into his fields to feed . . . " Luke 15:15
41 "And he arose, and came . . . his father" Luke 15:20
42 "and ran, and fell on his . . . " Luke 15:20
45 and 12 "make . . . as one of thy hired . . . " Luke 15:19
46 Demeanors
48 "and am . . . more worthy to be called thy son" Luke 15:21
50 "son was . . . , and is alive again" Luke 15:24
51 "Bring forth the . . . robe" Luke 15:22
52 Translation

VERTICAL

2 Son of Zerubbabel I Chron. 3:20
3 "and . . . every good piece of land with stones" II Kings 3:19
4 Turkish commander
5 "A certain man had two . . . " Luke 15:11
6 Drunkard
7 Adjective suffix (pl.)
8 Bone
9 Southern state
12 Cunning
13 "and . . .s on his feet" Luke 15:22
14 "Do ye . . . believe" John 16:31
16 "And he . . . unto them his living" Luke 15:12
18 "and took his journey into a . . . country" Luke 15:13
19 "And when he had . . . all" Luke 15:14
20 "And all that handle the . . . " Ezek. 27:29
21 "hired servants of my father's have . . . enough and to spare" Luke 15:17
22 King of Bashan Josh. 13:12
23 "there arose a mighty famine in that . . . " Luke 15:14
25 "ask, and . . . shall receive" John 16:24
31 "and there . . . his substance with riotous living" Luke 15:13
32 "Father, I have . . . against heaven, and in thy sight" Luke 15:21
35 Number of sons the man had
38 Eye (Scot.)
39 "he was . . . , and is found" Luke 15:24
40 "and he began to be in . . . " Luke 15:14
43 Taxi
44 Kine (Scot.)
45 Mother
47 Recording Secretary
49 "whether it be of God, . . . whether I speak of myself" John 7:17

"I say unto you, that likewise joy shall be in heaven over one sinner that repenteth, more than over ninety and nine just persons, which need no repentance." — Luke 15:7.

NUMBER 42

THE RICH YOUNG RULER

HORIZONTAL

2 ". . . give to the poor" Mark 10:21
4 "and . . . and follow me" Matt. 19:21
8 Lord Provost
10 See 52 down
11 "Go out quickly into the streets and . . . of the city" Luke 14:21
12 Small yellow bird
13 Recently extinct bird of New Zealand
15 A bandage for the head
16 Against; Veterinary Surgeon
17 Fifth month of the year (pl.)
19 Clergyman; centiliter
20 "This voice came not because of me, but for your . . . " John 12:30
22 "the disciples were astonished . . . his words" Mark 10:24
23 ". . . my yoke upon you, and learn of me" Matt. 11:29
25 "All these things have I kept from my youth . . . " Matt. 19:20
26 From
27 New England state
28 War heroes
29 Second note in scale
30 See 37 down
31 "sharp sword with two . . . " Rev. 2:12
33 Greek letter
34 Size of shot
36 "than for a rich man to enter into . . . kingdom of God" Matt. 19:24
38 "whosoever doth not bear his . . . , and come after me" Luke 14:27
41 Girl's name
43 South America
44 An art student (F.)
46 ". . . came one running" Mark 10:17
47 Mother
49 "hid themselves in the . . . and in the rocks" Rev. 6:15
50 Newspaper item
51 "... whatsoever thou hast" Mark 10:21
53 "... thou shalt have treasure in heaven" Mark 10:21
54 and 55 "My sheep hear my voice, and I know them, and they . . . . . . " John 10:27
A saying of Jesus is 2, 4, 23, 25, 36, 38, 53, 54, and 55 combined

VERTICAL

1 "Thou knowest the . . .s" Mark 10:19
2 "and went . . . grieved" Mark 10:22
3 Compass point
4 "Why . . . thou me good" Mark 10:18
5 "there is none good but . . . , that is, God" Mark 10:18
6 "they were astonished out of . . . " Mark 10:26
7 Plural ending of nouns
8 "Then Jesus beholding him . . . him" Mark 10:21
9 "for he had great . . . " Mark 10:22
11 "One thing thou . . ." Mark 10:21
14 "He promised with an . . . to give her whatsoever she would ask" Matt. 14:7
18 "for we have seen his . . . in the east" Matt. 2:2
21 Imitated
24 Sharp
32 "for my sake and the . . .s" Mark 10:29
35 Capital of Moab Num. 21:28
36 "I give unto you power to . . . on serpents and scorpions" Luke 10:19
37 and 30 across "how . . . is it for them that . . . in riches" Mark 10:24
38 "It is easier for a . . . to go through the eye of a needle" Mark 10:25
39 ". . . if he shall ask an egg, will he offer him a scorpion" Luke 11:12
40 "And he was . . . at that saying" Mark 10:22
42 Exclamation
45 "and . . . the world to come eternal life" Mark 10:30
48 "with God . . . things are possible" Mark 10:27
51 "as Jonas was a sign unto the Ninevites, . . . shall also the Son of man be" Luke 11:30
52 and 10 across ". . . , . . . have left all, and have followed thee" Mark 10:28

1		2	3			4	5	6	7		8	9
		10			11						12	
13	14			15							16	
17			18		19			20	21			
22			23	24				25			26	
27			28					29				
		30						31		32		
33				34			35					
		36	37			38		39	40			
41	42				43			44			45	
46						47	48		49			
		50			51			52				
53				54							55	

"But many that are first shall be last; and the last first." — Mark 10:31.

NUMBER 43

ZACCHAEUS ENTERTAINS JESUS

HORIZONTAL

1 "This day is . . . come to this house" Luke 19:9
7 Marry
10 "Do ye not . . . understand" Matt. 16:9
11 ". . . thy way; thy faith hath made thee whole" Mark 10:52
12 Image
14 Credit
15 "and received him . . . " Luke 19:6
16 Yea
17 "Behold . . . Israelite indeed, in whom is no guile" John 1:47
18 "and could not for the . . . " Luke 19:3
22 "the poison of . . .s is under their lips" Rom. 3:13
24 Exclamation of surprise
26 "An hundred measures of . . . " Luke 16:6 (pl.)
27 "which was the . . . among the publicans" Luke 19:2
29 Sun god
30 Wood sorrel
31 ". . . , every one that thirsteth" Isa. 55:1
32 Plural ending of nouns
33 Royal Highness
35 "there was a . . . named Zacchaeus" Luke 19:2
36 "for . . . day I must abide at thy house" Luke 19:5
38 An arched roof
39 "what ye hear in the . . . , that preach ye" Matt. 10:27
40 "Jesus saith unto . . . , Woman, believe me" John 4:21
41 See 34 down
44 "Eat not of it . . . , nor sodden at all with water" Ex. 12:9
47 "even . . . must the Son of man be lifted up" John 3:14
48 "because he was . . . of stature" Luke 19:3
51 "Blessed . . . the peacemakers" Matt. 5:9
52 Hebrew deity
53 "if I have taken any thing from any man by . . . accusation" Luke 19:8
54 "And Jesus . . . and passed through Jericho" Luke 19:1

VERTICAL

1 "and climbed up into a . . . tree" Luke 19:4
2 Eagle's nest
3 Lieutenant
4 "repented long . . . in sackcloth and ashes" Matt. 11:21
5 Plaything
6 Nothing
7 "for he was to pass that . . . " Luke 19:4
8 For example
9 "Zacchaeus, make haste, and come . . . " Luke 19:5
13 Milliliter
17 "bringing gold, and silver, ivory, and . . .s, and peacocks" I Kings 10:22
18 "I give to the . . ." Luke 19:8
19 "and he was . . . " Luke 19:2
20 Highest note in scale of Guido
21 Sunday School
22 "Then said I, . . . Lord God" Ezek. 4:14
23 "guest with a man that is a . . . " Luke 19:7
25 "And he made . . . , and came down" Luke 19:6
27 "the Son of man is . . . to seek and to save" Luke 19:10
28 "I restore him . . . " Luke 19:8
34 and 41 across "he looked . . . , and . . . him" Luke 19:5
37 ". . . else believe me for the very works' sake" John 14:11
40 "the . . . of my goods" Luke 19:8
41 Streets
42 Beverage
43 "that they may be one, even as . . . are one" John 17:22
44 "And he . . . before" Luke 19:4
45 "Rabbi, thou . . . the Son of God" John 1:49
46 Tiny
47 "And he sought to . . . Jesus" Luke 19:3
49 Iowa
50 Thallium

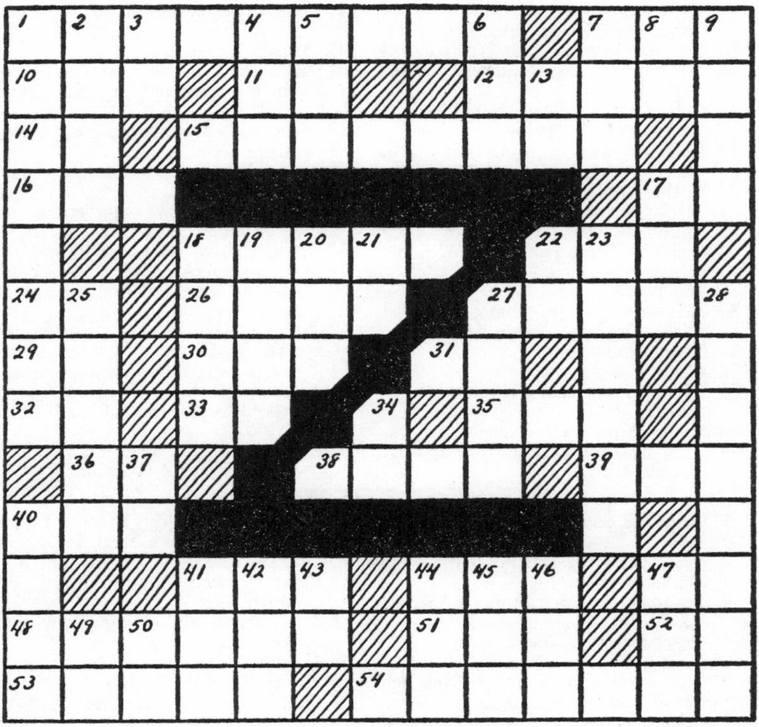

“For the Son of man is come to seek and to save that which was lost.” — Luke 19:10.

NUMBER 44

THE TRIUMPHAL ENTRY INTO JERUSALEM

HORIZONTAL

1 "saying, Who is..." Matt. 21:10
4 "behold, the world...gone after him" John 12:19
6 "but when...was glorified, then remembered they" John 12:16
10 To drag again
13 Associated Press; Apostle
14 "called the altar . . . "Josh. 22:34
16 "all the . . . was moved" Matt. 21:10
17 "when the unclean spirit had... him" Mark 1:26
19 "All this was . . . , that it might be fulfilled" Matt. 21:4
22 Ruthenium
24 Outfit of tools
25 "And . . . disciples went, and did as Jesus commanded them" Matt. 21:6
26 See 8 down
30 "Rejoice ye in that . . . , and leap for joy" Luke 6:23
31 Over again
33 Hebrew deity
35 "Behold, thy King...unto thee" Matt. 21:5
38 South America
39 ". . . into the village over against you" Matt. 21:2
40 The end of law
41 "as an . . . whose leaf fadeth" Isa. 1:30
43 "cometh in the name . . . the Lord" Matt. 21:9
45 "Ye seek Jesus of . . . " Mark 16:6
49 At sea
51 "a very great multitude . . . their garments in the way" Matt. 21:8
53 "The Lord hath . . . of them" Matt. 21:3
54 "and they...him thereon" Matt. 21:7
56 "And when he was come . . . Jerusalem" Matt. 21:10
57 "And if any man ask you, Why . . . ye loose him" Luke 19:31
59 ". . . the mount called the mount of Olives" Luke 19:29
60 ". . . , every one that thirsteth" Isa. 55:1
61 "Tell ye the daughter . . . Sion" Matt. 21:5
62 "walked by the sea of..." Mark 1:16
The multitude said 1, 4, 6, 25, 26, 43, 45, 61, and 62 combined

VERTICAL

1 "ye shall find an ass . . . " Matt. 21:2
2 A Benjamite I Chron. 7:12
3 Compass point
4 Grandson of Benjamin I Chron. 7:7
5 "whereon yet never man . . . " Luke 19:30
7 ". . . such things as are set before you" Luke 10:8
8 and 26 across "which was . . . by the . . . , saying," Matt. 21:4
9 "then . . . Jesus two disciples" Matt. 21:1
11 District of Columbia
12 A combining form signifying round
15 Period
18 "according to all the . . . of it" Num. 9:3
20 New High German
21 Eye (Scot.)
23 "All these things have I kept from my youth . . . " Matt. 19:20
26 Knave of clubs
27 Kind of grain
28 "He saith among the trumpets, . . . , . . . " Job 39:25
29 "I cannot dig; to . . . I am ashamed" Luke 16:3
30 "cut . . . branches" Matt. 21:8
32 "and strewed them in the . . . " Matt. 21:8
34 ". . . them, and bring them unto me" Matt. 21:2
35 Calcium
36 Browned slice of bread
37 "giving sound, whether pipe or . . . " I Cor. 14:7
42 Compound of tar and other substances
44 Compensation for services
46 "sitting upon an . . . " Matt. 21:5
47 "Were there not . . . cleansed" Luke 17:17
48 "Because the Lord . . . need of him" Luke 19:31
49 ". . . a colt with her" Matt. 21:2
50 "And which of you with taking thought can . . . to his stature one cubit" Luke 12:25
52 "found the colt tied by the . . . " Mark 11:4
55 Snakelike fish
58 King of Bashan Josh. 13:12
59 Indian plant producing dye

1		2	3	■	4	5	■	6	7	8		9
	■	10		11			12	■	13		■	
14	15	■	■	16				■	17		18	
19		20	21	■	■	■	22	23	■	24		
■	25			■	26	27			28			■
29	■		■	30			■	■	31			32
33	34	■	35				36	37	■	■	38	
39		■	40		■	■	41		42	■	■	
■	43	44	■	45	46					47	48	■
49			50	■		■	51					52
53				■	54	55		■	56			
	■	■	57	58	■		■	59		■	60	
■	61		■	62							■	

"And the multitudes that went before, and that followed, cried, saying, Hosanna to the Son of David: Blessed is he that cometh in the name of the Lord: Hosanna in the highest." — Matt. 21:9.

NUMBER 45

THE PARABLE OF THE TEN VIRGINS

HORIZONTAL

1 "And at . . . there was a cry made" Matt. 25:6
7 Township
9 "And . . . they went to buy" Matt. 25:10
11 "came also . . . other virgins, saying, Lord, Lord, open to us" Matt. 25:11
12 Brother
13 "but he that believeth not . . . condemned already" John 3:18
14 Number of Psalm beginning "O Lord, rebuke me not in thine anger"
16 "Give us of your . . . ; for our lamps are gone out" Matt. 25:8
17 "and went forth to meet the . . ." Matt. 25:1
22 Son of Bani Ezra 10:34
23 French
24 Girl's name
26 A very young hawk
27 "and there he . . . with them, and baptized" John 3:22
29 Spain
31 "But the wise took oil . . . their vessels" Matt. 25:4
32 Northwestern state
33 ". . . that were foolish took their lamps, and took no oil with them" Matt. 25:3
34 and 38 down "Then . . . those virgins . . . " Matt. 25:7
37 Age
38 "And . . . Moses lifted up the serpent in the wilderness" John 3:14
40 "Not . . . ; lest there be not enough for us and you" Matt. 25:9
41 Slept
45 "and the door was . . . " Matt. 25:10
47 Part in play
48 ". . . , I perceive that thou art a prophet" John 4:19
49 ". . . the foolish said unto the wise" Matt. 25:8
52 "But while men . . . , his enemy came" Matt. 13:25
54 "went in with him to the . . . " Matt. 25:10
55 Bah; a New Zealand stockade
Our text is 9, 11, 17, 27, 33, 34, 41, 49, and 52 combined

VERTICAL

1 Third note in scale
2 Suffix forming adjectives
3 "In my name shall they cast out . . . " Mark 16:17
4 "The wind bloweth where . . . listeth" John 3:8
5 Two fifths of Ghent
6 "This is my beloved Son: . . . him" Mark 9:7
7 "and . . . their lamps" Matt. 25:7
8 Chum
9 "And five of them were . . . " Matt. 25:2
10 Here lies (L.)
12 "and five were . . . " Matt. 25:2
15 The same (L.)
17 "and . . . for yourselves" Matt. 25:9
18 "and they that were . . . went in" Matt. 25:10
19 A small lizard
20 Bowl, or chalice
21 "And all that handle the . . . " Ezek. 27:29
25 Newspaper item
26 Ephesians
28 Royal Navy
29 Strain
30 "And he shook off the beast into the fire, and felt no . . . " Acts 28:5
35 Laboratory (college slang)
36 "Behold, the bridegroom . . . " Matt. 25:6
37 Evangelical Union
38 See 34 across
39 "but go ye rather to them that . . . " Matt. 25:9
41 A division of the Koran
42 Lieutenant
43 Ancestor of Jesus Luke 3:28
44 "Sir, thou hast nothing to draw with, and the well is . . . " John 4:11
46 "go ye out to meet . . . " Matt. 25:6
49 Capital of Moab Num. 21:28
50 Nickel
51 Danish
53 Father

■	■	1	2	3		4	5	6		■	7	8
9	10				■	11			■	12		
13		■	■	14	15	■	■		■	16		
	■	17	18			19	20		21			■
	■	22			■	23		■	24			25
■	26				■	27		28				
29		■		■	30	■	31		■	32		■
33				■	34	35		■	■		■	36
	■	■	■	37			■	38	39	■	40	
	■	41	42				43			44	■	
45	46			■	■	■	47				■	
48			■	49	50	51	■	52			53	
■	54								■	55		

"Watch therefore, for ye know neither the day nor the hour wherein the Son of man cometh." — Matt. 25:13.

NUMBER 46
THE PARABLE OF THE TALENTS
HORIZONTAL

1 ". . . wicked and slothful servant" Matt. 25:26
3 "reaping where thou . . . not sown" Matt. 25:24
6 Exclamation; owl's cry
9 Capital of Moab Num. 21:28
11 North America
12 "because ye have . . . with me from the beginning" John 15:27
13 "that thou art an . . . man" Matt. 25:24
16 " . . . , there thou hast that is thine" Matt. 25:25
17 "thou good and . . . servant" Matt. 25:21
19 "have thou authority . . . ten cities" Luke 19:17
21 "but . . . God with fastings and prayers night and day" Luke 2:37
23 "After . . . long time the lord of those servants cometh" Matt. 25:19
24 "for many be called, but . . . chosen" Matt. 20:16
27 "We have seen strange . . . today" Luke 5:26
29 "man travelling into a . . . country" Matt. 25:14
31 Ever (cont.)
32 Babylonian deity
33 ". . . should have received mine own with usury" Matt. 25:27
34 "Out of thine own mouth . . . I judge thee" Luke 19:22
36 ". . . not my Father's house an house of merchandise" John 2:16
39 Queen Victoria (L.); verb reflexive
41 Chinese measure
43 "and said, Lord, I knew . . . " Matt. 25:24
45 ". . . thou into the joy of thy lord" Matt. 25:21
48 "I have gained . . . other talents beside them" Matt. 25:22
51 "he will make him . . . over all that he hath" Luke 12:44
53 "Be thou also . . . five cities" Luke 19:19
57 ". . . God, thou art my God" Ps. 63:1
58 Large compressed packages
60 "thou knewest that I . . . where I sowed not" Matt. 25:26
62 "I have . . . things to say and to judge of you" John 8:26
63 "The . . . which are impossible with men are possible with God" Luke 18:27

Our text is 1, 3, 12, 17, 19, 23, 24, 27, 33, 34, 36, 43, 51, 53, 62, and 63 combined

VERTICAL

1 Candy
2 Part of the day
4 "thou art . . . austere man" Luke 19:21
5 Helmet worn during the fifteenth century
6 "For the kingdom of . . . is as" Matt. 25:14
7 Whirlwind off the Faroe Islands
8 Expert (slang)
10 His Royal Highness
13 "I was afraid, and went and . . . thy talent" Matt. 25:25
14 "and then . . . my coming" Matt. 25:27
15 Defender of the Faith
18 "Master, it is good for . . . to be here" Luke 9:33
19 A combining form signifying egg
20 "And they shall fall by the . . . of the sword" Luke 21:24
22 The fifth satellite of Saturn
23 Lava
25 Snakelike fish
26 "His lord said unto him, . . . done" Matt. 25:21
28 "traded with the . . . , and made them other five talents" Matt. 25:16
29 "unto one he gave . . . talents, to another two, and to another one" Matt. 25:15
30 Right Worthy
35 Almost all of Ireland
37 Knight Templar
38 Exclamation of inquiry
40 Royal Navy Reserve
42 "and give . . . unto him which hath ten talents" Matt. 25:28
44 Half an em
46 Bass horn
47 "because thou didst . . . on the Lord" II Chron. 16:8
49 Grief
50 Half of Ovid
52 Second note of scale
54 Sea eagle
55 Regular
56 "thou takest . . . that thou layedst not down" Luke 19:21
59 Street
61 "Inasmuch . . . ye have done it unto one of the least of these" Matt. 25:40

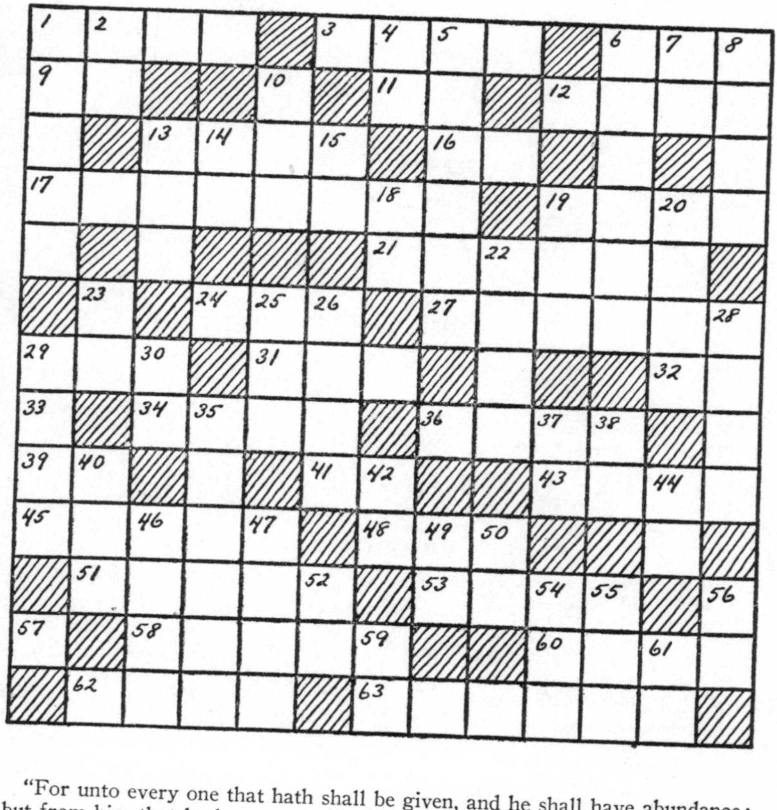

"For unto every one that hath shall be given, and he shall have abundance: but from him that hath not shall be taken away even that which he hath." — Matt. 25:29.

NUMBER 47
THE LAST SUPPER
HORIZONTAL

1 "which is . . . for many" Matt. 26:28
4 "I will not drink henceforth of this . . . of the vine" Matt. 26:29
8 King of Bashan Josh. 13:12
10 "And I will . . . the Father, and he shall give you another Comforter" John 14:16
12 "catch them in their net, and gather them in their . . . " Hab. 1:15
14 "Take . . . , and divide it among yourselves" Luke 22:17
15 "ye . . . shew the Lord's death till he come" I Cor. 11:26
16 "ye believe . . . God, believe also in me" John 14:1
17 Exclamation
18 Pineapple
20 "and blessed it, and . . . it" Matt. 26:26
21 "Ye shall . . . me" John 13:33
23 Yea
24 Rodent
25 The sesame (Hind.)
27 "Let not your heart . . . troubled" John 14:1
28 "when I drink . . . new with you in my Father's kingdom" Matt. 26:29
29 "and bring all things to your . . . " John 14:26
35 Diphthong
36 Small yellow bird
37 Last (L.)
39 Son of Nathan, descendant of Judah I Chron. 2:36
41 "even so must the Son of man be lifted . . . " John 3:14
42 "and they . . . drank of it" Mark 14:23
43 "If I then, . . . Lord and Master, have washed . . . feet" John 13:14
46 South America
47 "until the kingdom . . . God shall come" Luke 22:18
49 "Whither I go, thou canst not follow . . . now" John 13:36
50 "Then arose Peter, and . . . unto the sepulchre" Luke 24:12
51 Compass point
53 Man's name
56 ". . . thee behind me, Satan" Matt. 16:23
57 Second person singular of do
58 "for the remission of . . . " Matt. 26:28
A saying of Christ is 14, 15, 16, 29, 47, and 49 combined

VERTICAL

1 "if it were not . . . , I would have told you" John 14:2
2 Ephesians
3 ". . . ye all of it" Matt. 26:27
4 Exclamation expressing disapproval (var.)
5 A kind of Japanese salad
6 A Benjamite I Chron. 7:12
7 South American animal resembling the weasel
9 "and . . . it to the disciples" Matt. 26:26
11 A good king of Judah II Chron. 14:2
13 "which strain at a . . . , and swallow a camel" Matt. 23:24
14 "Verily I say unto you, They have . . . reward" Matt. 6:2
15 "until that . . . " Matt. 26:29
17 Oven (var.)
19 North America
20 "Jesus took . . . " Matt. 26:26
22 A son of Aaron Ex. 6:23
26 "Where wilt thou that . . . prepare for thee to eat the passover" Matt. 26:17
27 Bromine
28 Put *c* in front of this and in French it is heaven
30 The Last Supper was the Paschal . . .
31 Recently extinct bird of New Zealand
32 "Take, eat; this is my . . . " Matt. 26:26
33 "And he took the . . . " Matt. 26:27
34 "And as they were . . . " Matt. 26:26
38 "and gave . . . , and gave it to them, saying" Matt. 26:27
40 "For this is my . . . of the new testament" Matt. 26:28
41 ". . . of the Chaldees" Gen. 11:28
44 Leave out
45 Son of Bani Ezra 10:34
46 South America
48 "They reel to and . . . , and stagger" Ps. 107:27
50 Brazilian coin
52 Eye (Scot.)
54 Against
55 Linnaean Society

1		2	3		4		5	6	7		8	9
		10		11			12			13		
	14					15			16			
17			18		19			20				
21		22			23			24				
25				26			27				28	
	29		30		31	32				33		
34		35			36					37		38
		39		40					41			
		42				43	44	45			46	
				47	48		49			50		
51	52			53		54			55			
56				57					58			

"For as often as ye eat this bread, and drink this cup, ye do shew the Lord's death till he come." — I Cor. 11:26.

NUMBER 48

THE BETRAYAL AND ARREST OF JESUS

HORIZONTAL

1 ". . . how then shall the scriptures be fulfilled" Matt. 26:54
3 "if it be possible, let . . . cup pass from me" Matt. 26:39
7 "he . . . at hand that doth betray me" Matt. 26:46
9 "meat offering baken in a . . . " Lev. 2:5
10 "Put up thy sword into the . . . " John 18:11
11 A part of knowledge
13 "betrayest thou the Son of man with a . . . " Luke 22:48
15 Printers' measure
17 "have ye not read in the . . . " Matt. 12:5
18 Is it (cont.)
20 "that same is he; . . . him, and lead him away safely" Mark 14:44
22 "Sleep on now, and take . . . rest" Matt. 26:45
24 "the . . . is at hand" Matt. 26:45
26 Ancestor of Jesus Luke 3:28
27 Recording Secretary
28 Linear measure used in Turkey
29 Civil Engineer
30 Doctor of Laws (L.)
31 "and with him a . . . multitude" Matt. 26:47
33 Africa
34 "as an old lion; who shall . . . him up" Gen. 49:9
37 ". . . therefore ye seek me, let these go their way" John 18:8
38 Odor, a combining form
40 "stretched out his hand, . . . drew his sword" Matt. 26:51
41 "Then all . . . disciples forsook him, and fled" Matt. 26:56
42 "Son of man sitting on the right hand of . . . " Matt. 26:64
43 Affirmatives
45 "and said unto them, Whom . . . ye" John 18:4
46 "and come . . . of the glory of God" Rom. 3:23
49 Capital of Moab Num. 21:28
51 Doctor of Divinity
53 High priest and judge of Israel I Sam. 1:9
54 "Thou hast given a . . . to them that fear thee" Ps. 60:4
56 "more than twelve legions . . . angels" Matt. 26:53
57 "from the sixth hour there was . . . over all the land unto the ninth hour" Matt. 27:45

A saying of Christ is 1, 3, 7, 22, 24, 40, 41, 42, 56, and 57 combined

VERTICAL

1 Security
2 Not say
3 "they laid . . . hands on him, and took him" Mark 14:46
4 "upon the . . . of the robe pomegranates" Ex. 39:24
5 Iowa
6 Saints
8 "For God . . . loved the world" John 3:16
9 Peck
12 "Friend, . . . art thou come" Matt. 26:50
14 "with . . . and staves for to take me" Matt. 26:55
16 "and smote off his . . . " Matt. 26:51
19 "Are ye come out as against a . . . " Matt. 26:55
20 Tungsten
21 "and the Son of man is . . . into the hands of sinners" Matt. 26:45
23 "Who gave himself for . . . " Titus 2:14
25 Edible tuber of Peru and Bolivia
28 "Smote a servant of the high . . . " Mark 14:47
29 "Then . . . they, and laid hands on Jesus" Matt. 26:50
30 "lo, . . . , one of the twelve, came" Matt. 26:47
32 "daily with you in the temple teaching, and ye . . . me not" Mark 14:49
35 "And . . . of them that stood by drew a sword" Mark 14:47
36 And (F.)
39 Compass point
42 Nut
44 ". . . hath done what . . . could" Mark 14:8
47 "bringeth forth out of his treasure things new and . . . " Matt. 13:52
48 Royal Irish Academy
49 Answer
50 Thing
52 "That thou doest, . . . quickly" John 13:27
54 Book
55 New England

■	1	2		■	3	4	5	6	■	7	8	■
9			■	10						■	11	12
13			14	■	15		■		■	16	■	
■	17			■	18		19	■	20			
21	■	22		23		■	24	25			■	
26		■	27		■	28			■	■	29	
	■	30		■	31				32	■	33	
34	35			36	■	37		■	38	39		
40			■	41			■	42				
43			44	■	■	45				■	■	
	■	46		47	48		■		■	49	50	■
51	52	■	53			■	54		55			
■	56		■	57								■

"Are ye come out, as against a thief, with swords and with staves to take me?" — Mark 14:48.

NUMBER 49

JESUS BEFORE PILATE

HORIZONTAL

1 "that . . . should bear witness unto the truth" John 18:37
2 "seek, and ye shall . . . " Matt. 7:7
6 "Sayest thou this thing of thyself, or did . . . tell it thee of me" John 18:34
13 "judge him according to your . . . " John 18:31
14 Plant, much used in hedges
15 Three-toed sloths
17 Father
18 East Indies
19 High priest and judge of Israel I Sam. 14:3
20 "and immediately the cock . . . " John 18:27
22 Royal Navy
24 Grandfather of Saul I Chron. 8:33
25 and 26 "I find in him . . . . . . at all" John 18:38
29 Capital of Moab Num. 21:28
30 "but a broken spirit . . . the bones" Prov. 17:22
31 "and the third day he shall . . . again" Luke 18:33
32 South America
34 "And Simon Peter followed Jesus, and so . . . another disciple" John 18:15
35 And (F.)
36 Sour substances
37 Whirlwind off the Faroe Islands
38 Translation
40 Size of shot
41 "and went . . . with Jesus into the palace of the high priest" John 18:15
42 "for . . . cause came I into the world" John 18:37
44 "at the valley of Shaveh, which is the king's . . . " Gen. 14:17
47 A little pocket for a watch
49 A city of Benjamin I Chron. 8:12
51 "then would my servants . . . " John 18:36
54 Days in Roman calendar
56 "I have also called my mighty . . . for mine anger" Isa. 13:3
57 A Benjamite I Chron. 7:12
58 "signifying what . . . he should die" John 18:32
59 Great
60 "It is not lawful for us to put any . . . to death" John 18:31
A saying of Pilate is 1, 2, 25, 26, 41, 42, and 60 combined

VERTICAL

3 He (F.)
4 A short sleep
5 Stunted
6 Open (poetic)
7 "And others had . . . of cruel mockings and scourgings" Heb. 11:36
8 Exclamation
9 "at . . . , or at midnight, or at the cock-crowing, or in the morning" Mark 13:35
10 "will ye therefore that I . . . unto you the King of the Jews" John 18:39
11 "He . . . up the people" Luke 23:5
12 ". . . , thou hast nothing to draw with" John 4:11
15 "What . . . bring ye against this man" John 18:29
16 "when the Comforter is come, whom I will . . . unto you" John 15:26
21 "My kingdom is not of this . . . " John 18:36
23 "Thine own . . . and the chief priests have delivered thee unto me" John 18:35
27 German painter
28 "Pilate saith unto him, What is . . . " John 18:38
33 "the . . . of violence is in their hands" Isa. 59:6
39 Fissure
41 Namely
43 "...that Pilate marvelled" Mark 15:5
44 "what hast thou..." John 18:35
45 ". . . they should be defiled" John 18:28
46 "Art thou the . . . of the Jews" John 18:33
48 "To this end was I . . . " John 18:37
50 Bow
51 Field Officer
52 ". . . thee behind me, Satan" Luke 4:8
53 Here lies (L.)
55 Babylonian deity
57 Iowa

1	■	2	3	4	5	■	6	7	8	9	10	11
■	12	■	13			■	14					
15		16	■	17		■	18		■	19		
20			21	■	22	23	■		■	24		
	■	25		■	26		27		28	■	29	
	■	30						■	31			
32	33	■		■	34			■		■	35	
36					■	37		■	38	39	■	
40		■	■	■	41		■	42			43	■
	■	44		45		■	46	■	■	47		48
49	50		■		■	51		52	53		■	
54			55		■	56				■	57	
■	58					■	59		■	60		

"To this end was I born, and for this cause came I into the world, that I should bear witness unto the truth. Every one that is of the truth heareth my voice." — John 18:37.

NUMBER 50

THE DEATH OF CHRIST

HORIZONTAL

1 "And, behold, the . . . of the temple was rent in twain" Matt. 27:51
3 Dean of the Faculty
6 Small child
8 A priest I Chron. 24:8
10 North America
12 "And they . . . him" Matt. 27:35
14 Small lizards
17 Kine (Scot.)
18 Royal Horse Artillery
19 "and parted his . . . " Matt. 27:35
21 Defender of the Faith (L.)
22 Capital of Moab Num. 21:28
23 Second note in scale
24 Nickel
26 "My God, my God, why hast thou . . . me" Matt. 27:46
30 Southwest
32 "Truly this was the . . . of God" Matt. 27:54
33 "Father, into thy hands I commend my . . . " Luke 23:46
35 "and the . . . did quake, and the rocks rent" Matt. 27:51
37 Promissory note
38 Son of Noah Gen. 5:32
40 Jesus . . . the passover with the disciples
42 A chief of Naphtali Num. 1:15
43 "What I have . . . I have . . . " John 19:22
46 A waxy substance
47 Edges of the roof
48 "for we receive the due reward of our . . . " Luke 23:41
50 "This title . . . read many of the Jews" John 19:20
51 Egyptian goddess
52 "Then were there . . . thieves crucified with him" Matt. 27:38

VERTICAL

1 "took a sponge, and filled it with . . . " Matt. 27:48
2 "and it was written . . . Hebrew, and Greek, and Latin" John 19:20
3 "from the sixth hour there was . . . over all the land unto the ninth hour" Matt. 27:45
4 "every good tree bringeth forth good . . . " Matt. 7:17
5 Servant of Solomon Ezra 2:57
6 "And it was the . . . hour" Mark 15:25
7 ". . . . . . shalt thou be with me in paradise" Luke 23:43
8 House of Commons
9 Frosts
11 "many women were there beholding . . . off" Matt. 27:55
13 Exclamation of inquiry
15 Transpose
16 State Militia
20 "ye therefore do greatly . . . " Mark 12:27
21 "It is . . . " John 19:30
24 Grandfather of Saul I Chron. 8:33
25 "Thou shalt love thy neighbour . . . thyself" Matt. 19:19
26 "Father, . . . them; for they know not what they do" Luke 23:34
27 Ontario
28 Attaches
29 "among his own . . . , and in his own house" Mark 6:4
31 ". . . , behold thy son" John 19:26
32 South America
34 "saith, I . . . " John 19:28
36 "these men were bound in their coats, their hosen, and their . . . " Dan. 3:21
39 A son of Gad Gen. 46:16
41 Tellurium
42 War heroes
43 "let it be . . . with the dew of heaven" Dan. 4:15
44 Hurrah
45 "Were there not . . . cleansed" Luke 17:17
49 East Indies

1		2			3	4		5		6		7
				8			9					
10	11			12							13	
14		15	16		17					18		
19				20					21			
22				23				24			25	
		26	27			28	29				30	31
	32				33					34		
35				36		37			38		39	
				40	41			42				
43	44		45					46				
47						48	49					
50					51					52		

"And Pilate wrote a title, and put it on the cross. And the writing was, JESUS OF NAZARETH THE KING OF THE JEWS." — John 19:19.

NUMBER 51

THE RESURRECTION

HORIZONTAL

1 "they saw that the . . . was rolled away" Mark 16:4
5 "in shining . . .s" Luke 24:4
11 A combining form indicating relation to an early period of time
12 A son of Gad Gen. 46:16
13 "and seeth the linen clothes . . . " John 20:6
14 ". . . else he will hold to the one and despise the other" Matt. 6:24
15 "behold the . . . where they laid him" Mark 16:6
17 "tell his disciples that he is . . . from the dead" Matt. 28:7
18 Salad (Japanese)
19 And (F.)
20 "for I . . . not yet ascended to my Father" John 20:17
22 "But go your . . . , tell his disciples and Peter" Mark 16:7
26 "and . . . first to the sepulchre" John 20:4
28 "Come, . . . the place where the Lord lay" Matt. 28:6
29 "Sir, if thou have borne him hence, . . . me where thou hast laid him" John 20:15
31 Part of the day
33 "Deliver thyself as a . . . from the hand of the hunter" Prov. 6:5
34 "Who shall . . . us away the stone" Mark 16:3
38 "I . . . unto my Father, and your Father" John 20:17
40 Give out
41 Africa
43 Salutation (slang)
44 Average
45 Chinese measure (pl.)
47 Greek letter
50 "They were . . . , and bowed down their faces to the earth" Luke 24:5
52 Second note in scale
53 Decreased
55 "saw a young man sitting on the right . . ." Mark 16:5
56 Diphthong
57 "for it was very . . ." Mark 16:4
58 "seven ears of corn came up upon one stalk, . . . and good" Gen. 41:5

VERTICAL

1 "came unto the . . . at the rising of the sun" Mark 16:2
2 "and . . . all these things unto the eleven" Luke 24:9
3 With a king this is necking
4 "Sir, come down . . . my child die" John 4:49
6 . . . Baba, hero in Arabian Nights
7 "and the third day . . . again" Luke 24:7
8 "the whole city came out to . . . Jesus" Matt. 8:34
9 "I find . . . fault in this man" Luke 23:4
10 "for they . . . and were amazed" Mark 16:8
16 Dialect of Eastern Assam
21 "Touch . . . not" John 20:17
22 Writer to the Signet
23 Same as 56 across
24 "said unto the women, Fear not . . ." Matt. 28:5
25 "He is not . . . , but is risen" Luke 24:6
27 Odor
30 "clothed in a . . . white garment" Mark 16:5
32 "he planteth an . . ." Isa. 44:14
35 "Why seek ye the . . . among the dead" Luke 24:5
36 Lieutenant
37 "the . . . of my goods I give to the poor" Luke 19:8
39 Ember
42 "upon the . . . day of the week" Luke 24:1
46 South American monkey
48 "Ye . . . Jesus of Nazareth" Mark 16:6
49 "seeth . . . angels in white sitting" John 20:12
50 George . . . , an American writer
51 The same
52 "So they . . . both together" John 20:4
54 Ancestor of Jesus Luke 3:28

1	2		3	4		5	6	7	8		9	10
11			12				13				14	
15		16				17						
18								19			20	
			21		22	23	24			25		
26	27				28				29		30	
31								32		33		
34		35	36		37		38		39			
40					41	42		43				
	44				45		46		47			48
49				50				51			52	
53			54			55					56	
		57							58			

"And go quickly, and tell his disciples that he is risen from the dead; and, behold, he goeth before you into Galilee; there shall ye see him: lo, I have told you." — Matt. 28:7.

NUMBER 52
APPEARANCES AFTER THE RESURRECTION
HORIZONTAL

1 Penny; Court
3 "took bread, and . . . it, and brake" Luke 24:30
9 Perfect (tense)
11 "opened their mouth wide against me, and said, ...,...," Ps. 35:21
13 "he shewed himself . . . after his passion" Acts 1:3
14 "Sir, come down . . . my child die" John 4:49
15 Pinch
16 "as ye walk and are . . ." Luke 24:17
17 Golf mound
18 "Why . . . ye troubled" Luke 24:38
19 "their eyes were opened, and . . . knew him" Luke 24:31
21 "After . . . , he was seen of James" I Cor. 15:7
22 Sunday School
23 "incline thine . . . unto me" Ps. 17:6
26 "cried with a loud voice, and said, . . . Lord God" Ezek. 11:13
27 South Carolina
29 "He saith among the trumpets, . . . , . . ." Job 39:25
31 "and that believing ye might . . . life" John 20:31
33 "the disciples knew . . . that it was Jesus" John 21:4
35 "After that, he was . . . of above five hundred" I Cor. 15:6
37 "and how he was known . . . them in breaking . . . bread" Luke 24:35
38 William . . . Gladstone
40 "but when thou shalt be . . . , thou shalt stretch forth thy hands" John 21:18
41 "as they thus . . . , Jesus himself stood in the midst of them" Luke 24:36
42 Holy Mother Church (L.)
43 ". . . saith unto them, Peace be unto you" Luke 24:36
45 "while they . . . believed not for joy" Luke 24:41
46 "a spirit hath not flesh and bones, as ye see me . . ." Luke 24:39
48 Southeast
50 ". . . ye into all the world" Mark 16:15
51 Entomology
53 Label
55 "Jesus himself drew . . ." Luke 24:15
57 "and . . . they were not able to draw it" John 21:6
58 "because thou hast seen me, thou hast . . ." John 20:29
59 "shall . . . come in like manner" Acts 1:11

A saying of Jesus is 3, 18, 19, 21, 31, 33, 35, 43, 45, 46, and 58 combined

VERTICAL

1 Jesus' first miracle was performed at . . .
2 "to day is the . . . day since these things were done" Luke 24:21
4 Holds out
5 Valley in Judah where David slew Goliath I Sam. 17:2
6 "Cast the net on the right . . . of the ship" John 21:6
7 Under the title (L.); Holy Virgin (L.)
8 Snakelike fish
9 "that repentance and remission of sins should be . . . in his name" Luke 24:47
10 "he shewed them his hands and his . . ." Luke 24:40
12 "bringing gold, and silver, ivory, and . . .s, and peacocks" I Kings 10:22
14 Ethiopic
20 "these are written, that . . . might believe" John 20:31
21 Transpose
22 "Feed my . . ." John 21:16
24 "they looked stedfastly toward heaven . . . he went up" Acts 1:10
25 The doubting disciple
26 Average
27 Serpent
28 Pond-snail of genus Planorbis
30 "The hireling fleeth, because he is . . . hireling" John 10:13
32 Africa
34 Size of shot
35 Body
36 "Afterward he appeared unto the . . ." Mark 16:14
39 "while he talked with us by the . . ." Luke 24:32
41 South Dakota
42 "Jesus stood on the . . ." John 21:4
44 "yet was not the . . . broken" John 21:11
47 Grandson of Adam Gen. 4:26
49 "he is of . . . ; ask him" John 9:21
50 Almost gave
52 ". . . of them went that same day to a village" Luke 24:13
54 Month in Hebrew calendar
55 Nickel
56 Eye (Scot.)

1	2	■	3	4	5	6	7	8		■	9	10
11		12	■	13					■	14		
15			■	16			■		■	17		
18			■	19			20	■	21			
■		■	22		■	■	23	24		■		■
25	■	26		■	27	28	■		■	■	29	30
31	32			■	33		34	■	35	36		
37		■	38	39				■	40			■
	■	41					■	42			■	■
43	44		■	45			■	46			47	■
48		■	49	■	■	■	50		■	51		52
■	53	54		■	55	56			■	57		
■	■	58								■	59	

"Teaching them to observe all things whatsoever I have commanded you: and, lo, I am with you alway, even unto the end of the world." — Matt. 28:30.

SOLUTIONS

No. 1

J	E	S	U	S			K	E	E	P	E	R
E	E	L		D	O		I	N	N		L	O
W	R	E	N		W	E	N	T		O	N	O
S		W	O	K	E		G	E	S	H	A	M
	H		N		D	E		R	E		A	
J	U	D	E	A		R			L	A	M	B
O	R	E		N	O		W	I	F	E		E
S		M	A	N	G	E	R		L		O	H
E	G	O		A		T	A	X	E	D		O
P	A	C	S		S	A	P		S	O	U	L
H	E	R	O	D			P	A	S	S		D
	L	A	N	E	S		E	L		E	S	
O	S	T		W	O	R	D	L	E	S	S	

No. 2

	J	O	Y		S	T	A	R		E	O	N
		F			A	I	N		K	A	D	I
	A		E		I	N		W	I	S	E	
	M	E	N		D		S	E	N	T		J
G	I	F	T	S		A		N	G		B	E
R		T	E	E				T		Y	E	W
E	D		R		W	A	Y		N	E	T	S
A	R	M	S		O	L	D				H	
T	E	A		I	R	E			G	O	L	D
	A	R	E		S	E	E		O	R	E	
	M	Y	R	R	H		D				H	
L			E		I	N	E	R	M		E	
O	N	E		O	P	E	N	E	D		M	

No. 3

S		**O**	**N**			**E**	**A**	**R**	**T**	**H**		K
H	O	S	T	S				A	A		B	E
E	L			A	F	R	A	I	D		R	E
P	E	T	S		I	E	R	S		R	I	P
H	A	I		**P**	**E**	**A**	**C**	**E**		A	N	I
E		D	E	A	L	T			S	I	G	N
R	E	I		O	D	A	L			V		G
D	A	N		L			A	N	G	E	L	
S		**G**	**O**	**O**	**D**		**W**	**I**	**L**	**L**		
	A	S	K		A	L		G	O		A	B
N	C		S	A	V	E		H	R		L	O
O	R	S		E	I	G	H	T	Y		O	R
T	**O**	**W**	**A**	**R**	**D**		E	S		**M**	**E**	**N**

No. 4

O	N	T	O		L	I	G	H	T		S	
F	**O**	**R**		**M**	**I**	**N**	**E**		**E**	**Y**	**E**	**S**
F		A	S	O	K		N	E	E		T	E
E		P	A	R	E	N	T	S		E	T	A
R	E		L	A	W		I	S	R	A	E	L
				L	I	S	L	E		S	T	
H	**A**	**V**	**E**		**S**	**E**	**E**	**N**		**T**	**H**	**Y**
E	N	E		B	E		S	C	S			E
A	N	I	S	E		A		E	I	G	H	T
V	A	N		A	C	T	S		M		E	
E				G	A	L	I	L	E	E		T
N		**S**	**A**	**L**	**V**	**A**	**T**	**I**	**O**	**N**		W
S		C	H	E	E	S	E		N		S	O

No. 5

A		A	N	D		J	E	S	U	S		T
M		L	O		G	E	R		S	O		W
A		I	N	C	R	E	A	S	E	D		E
Z	E	B		S	E			A		O	W	L
E		I	N		W	I	S	D	O	M		V
D	P		O	F		N	E				M	E
	A	N	D		S	T	A	T	U	R	E	
S	N			W	O	O		E		O		U
A	N	D		I	N		F	A	V	O	U	R
Y	E	A	R	S		R	A			M	N	S
I		W	I	T	H		G	O	D		D	I
N	U	N			A	H		R	I	P	E	N
G	S		A	N	D		M	A	N		R	E

No. 6

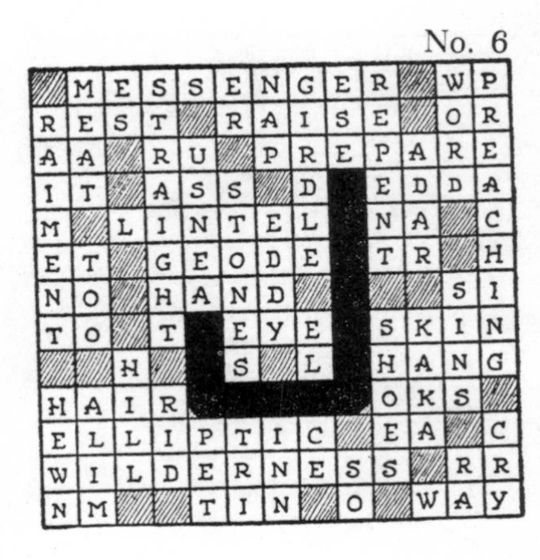

No. 7

T	H	I	S		I	S		M	Y		S	S
I				M		T	O	B	I	J	A	H
S	U	F	F	E	R		H		D	O	V	E
	S	U	R		H	E	M			H	E	R
B	E	L	O	V	E	D		S	O	N		E
A		F	M		A	D	A	P	T		E	Z
P	S	I		A		A	N	I		H	U	E
T	I	L	E	S			T	R	E	E		R
I	N		W	H	O	M		I		A	M	
Z		W	E	R	E		E	T		V	A	N
E	S		S	I		I	V		M	E	R	E
D	A	Y		E		M	I		A	N	N	E
	W	E	L	L		P	L	E	A	S	E	D

No. 8

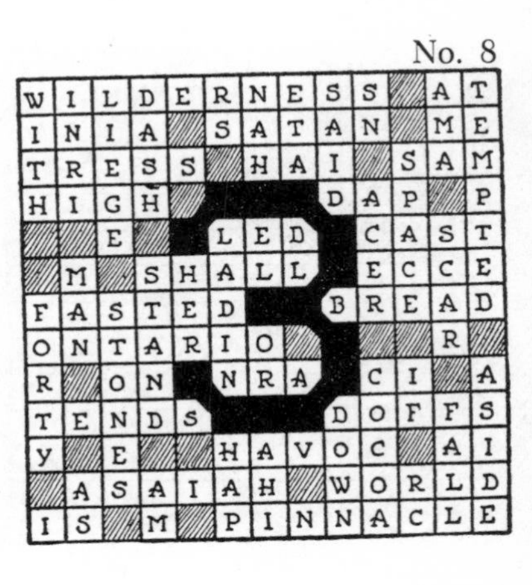

No. 9

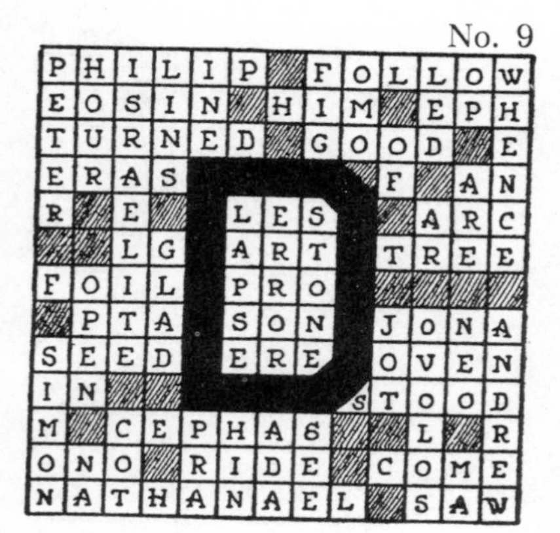

P	H	I	L	I	P		F	O	L	L	O	W
E	O	S	I	N		H	I	M		E	P	H
T	U	R	N	E	D		G	O	O	D		E
E	R	A	S						F		A	N
R		E			L	E	S			A	R	C
		L	G		A	R	T		T	R	E	E
F	O	I	L		P	R	O					
	P	T	A		S	O	N		J	O	N	A
S	E	E	D		E	R	E		O	V	E	N
I	N							S	T	O	O	D
M		C	E	P	H	A	S			L		R
O	N	O		R	I	D	E		C	O	M	E
N	A	T	H	A	N	A	E	L		S	A	W

No. 10

	W	**H**	**A**	**T**	**S**	**O**	**E**	**V**	**E**	**R**		W
M	I	A	M	I	S		L	A	G		G	A
A	N	D		R		F	I	L	L		A	T
R	E		H	E	R	E		E	A	G	L	E
R		**H**	**E**		**S**	**A**	**I**	**T**	**H**		I	R
I	D	O	L	S		S	A			A	L	P
A	R	U	M		M	T		B			E	O
G	A	R		A	O		R	E	G	R	E	T
E	W		**U**	**N**	**T**	**O**		**Y**	**O**	**U**		S
		S		T	H	E	E		O	L	D	
	W	O	R	S	E		W	A	D	E	R	S
C	A	N	A		R	I	E	M		R	E	I
I	S		**D**	**O**		N		**I**	**T**		E	X

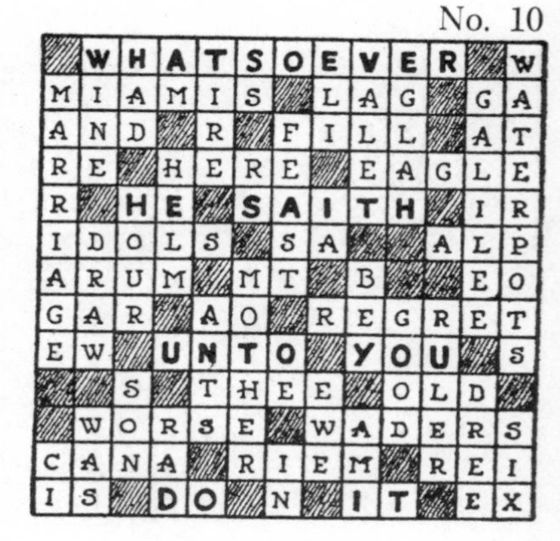

No. 11

	E	**X**	**C**	**E**	**P**	**T**		**A**		**M**	**A**	**N**
S	N		R		O	A	R		N		S	O
A	T	L	A	S			T	H	I	S		
B	**E**		**B**	**O**	**R**	**N**		**A**	**G**	**A**	**I**	**N**
T	R	Y		N				T	H	Y		A
A		E	D		K	R	C		T		A	M
H	**E**		**C**	**A**	**N**	**N**	**O**	**T**		**S**	**E**	**E**
	G	R		T	O		A	H	E	R		D
R	O	O	T		W	A	T	E	R		D	
U		**T**	**H**	**E**		**K**	**I**	**N**	**G**	**D**	**O**	**M**
L	A	T	A	N	I	A	S			L	E	U
E	V	E	N	T		N		D	R	O	S	S
R	A	N		**O**	**F**		**G**	**O**	**D**		T	T

No. 12

C		**W**	**H**	**O**	**S**	**O**	**E**	**V**	**E**	**R**		W
E	L			B	E	A	R			I	S	O
L		**D**	**R**	**I**	**N**	**K**	**E**	**T**	**H**		T	R
L	I	F	E		S	S		R	O	W	E	D
O	**F**		**T**	**H**	**E**		**W**	**A**	**T**	**E**	**R**	
		S	A	C		W	A	S		L	I	T
T	**H**	**A**	**T**		**I**		**S**	**H**	**A**	**L**	**L**	
A	R	T		S		G	T		M		E	S
L	E		**G**	**I**	**V**	**E**		**H**	**I**	**M**		P
K		T	O	N		R	S	A		I	R	I
E	P	H		**S**	**H**	**A**	**L**	**L**		S	I	R
D	E	E	P		E	R	I	A		E	P	I
	N	**E**	**V**	**E**	**R**		**T**	**H**	**I**	**R**	**S**	**T**

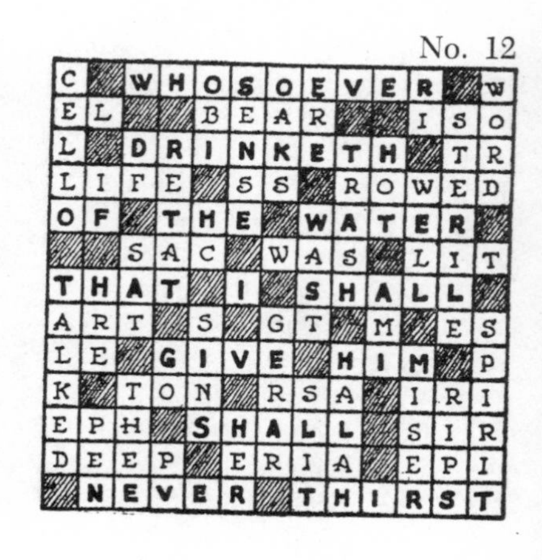

No. 13

No. 14

F	O	L	L	O	W		J	A	M	E	S	
I	L	E		N	E		O	M	A	R		Z
S	I	F	T			S	H	I	P	S		E
H	O	T		D	O	W	N			E	B	B
E			S	A	T				O		R	E
R	R		T	W	O		N		S	C	A	D
S	I	M	O	N		M	O		M	A	K	E
	S	E	A		L	E	T		O	S	E	E
M	E	N							T			
A	N	D	R	E	W		U		S	I		N
N		I		D	E	E	P		A	N	T	E
S	O	N		E	R	E		N	I	G	H	T
E		G	O	N	E		H	A	D		E	S

No. 15

R		**S**	**O**	**N**		**B**	**E**		**O**	**F**		H
O	A	R		A	L	O	N	E			G	O
O	N		P		E		D		A	B		U
M		F	A	I	T	H		H		O	O	S
	G	**O**	**O**	**D**		**C**	**H**	**E**	**E**	**R**		E
W	A	U	L		R	M		A		N	O	T
A		R	O	S	E		T	R	E	E		O
Y	E			N	A	S	U	T	E		S	P
	T	**H**	**Y**		**S**	**I**	**N**	**S**		**B**	**E**	
R	E	E		C	O	C	A		H	E	A	L
O		B	R	I	N	K		H	A	D		I
O	L	E	A				R	E	S		I	N
F	**O**	**R**	**G**	**I**	**V**	**E**	**N**		**T**	**H**	**E**	**E**

No. 16

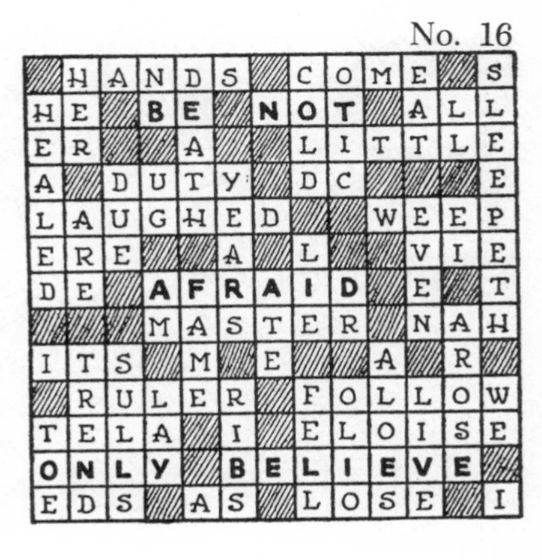

No. 17

No. 18

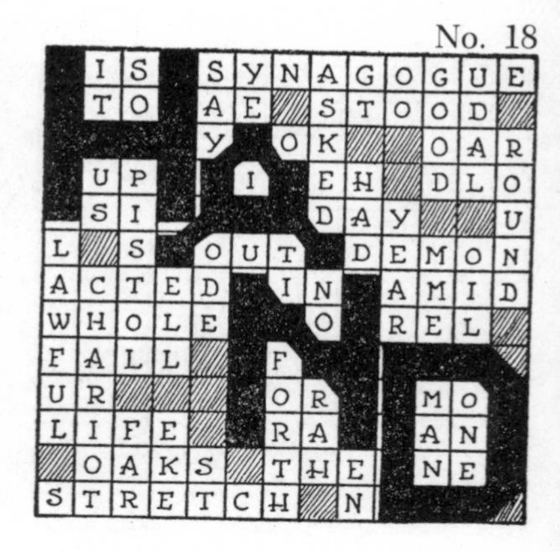

No. 19

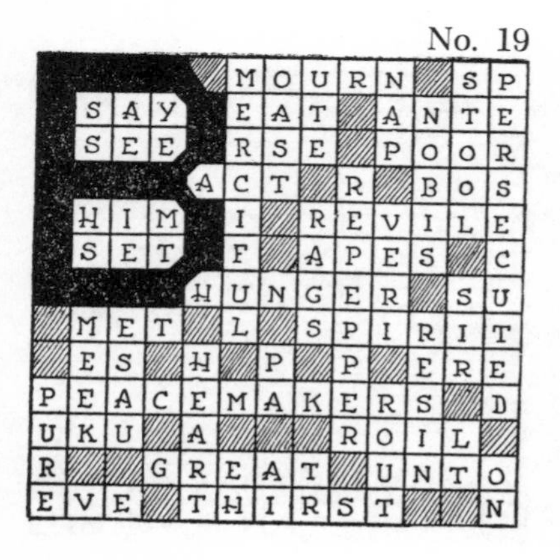

No. 20

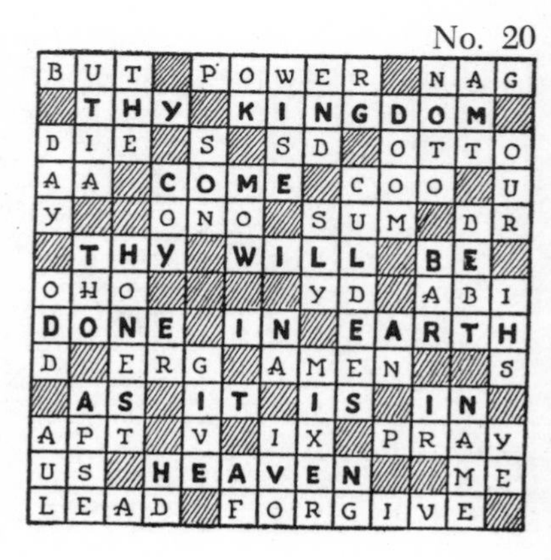

No. 21

R	I	G	H	T	L	Y		K	N	O	W	N
	R	I		H	O		S	I		I	A	L
F	O	R	G	A	V	E		S	I	N	S	
A	N	D		T	E	A	R	S		T	H	E
I	S				D				A	M		A
T		T	B				S		M	E	A	T
H		W	O		W		O		O	N	E	
		O	X		E		M		S	T		G
S	W			M	E		E					O
H	A	I	R		P		W	O	M	A	N	
A	T		O	B	I		H	O	U	S	E	
F	E	E	T		N	R	A		C	S		A
T	R	E	E		G	E	T		H	E	A	D

No. 22

B	E	H	O	L	D		C	H	O	K	E	D
E	A	R	T	H		I				I	R	I
A	R		I	D		T	H	O	R	N	S	
R	S		C		G			U	R	G	E	S
E		A		S	O	W	E	R		D		C
T	P			W	O	R	D		S	O	L	O
H	A	L	F		D		G	R		M	E	R
	R	O	O	T		S	E	E	D			C
F	A		W	E	N	T		F	O	R	T	H
A	B	E	L		J	O	Y		C	A	R	E
L	L		S	T		N	E	C	K	S		D
L	E	A		W	A	Y		O	S	E	E	
	S	T	O	O	D		T	O		S	O	W

No. 23

	B	U	T		G	A	T	H	E	R		H
S	U	N		D	O	M	A	I	N		M	A
A	R	T		D	O		R	E	E	L	E	R
	N	I	P		D	O	E		M	O		V
R	E	L	I	C			S	A	Y		N	E
E	D		T	U	N	A		R		S	O	S
A		T	H	E		W	H	E	A	T		T
P	O				O		A	S		E	H	
E		F	O	R	T	H			S	E	E	D
R		R	O	O	T		M	O	O		A	O
S	O	U		M	O	N	A		W		V	N
	W	I	S	P		A	N	A		S	E	E
I	N	T	O		M	Y		B	A	R	N	

No. 24

T		H	O	W		I	S		I	T		A
E	G		D	I	S	C	I	P	L	E		S
M	I	X	E	N			D	E	L	E		L
P	R			D	O	W	E	R	S		L	E
E	D	E	N		B	A		I		W	O	E
S		R	E	S	E	T		S	E	A		P
T	H	A	T		Y	E		H	A	V	E	
	I		S	T		R	S		S	E	E	M
G	N	U		H	A		A	W	E	S		A
R	D		R	E	B	U	K	E	D		P	N
E	E	N		R	I	T	E			M	A	N
A	R	O	S	E		I		C	E	A	S	E
T		N	O		F	A	I	T	H		S	R

No. 25

	M	Y		N	A	M	E		I	S		F
M		A	F	A	R		N	I		T	E	E
A	R	M	E	T		S		T	H	E	R	E
R	E	A	L			W	O		S	E	N	D
V			L	E	G	I	O	N		P	S	I
E	T	A		R	A	N			S			N
L	A		S	I	D	E		F	E		O	G
	M	E			A		S	L	A	G		
T	E		F	O	R		W	E		A	M	A
O		P	E	T	E	R		D	A	M	E	S
M	I	N	D		N	O	E		W	I	T	H
B	E			A	E	O	L	I	A	N		
S		A	R	E		M	A	N	Y		G	O

No. 26

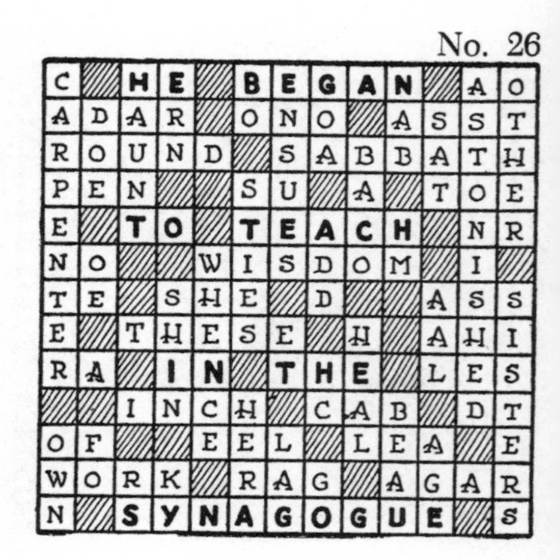

C		H	E		B	E	G	A	N		A	O
A	D	A	R		O	N	O		A	S	S	T
R	O	U	N	D		S	A	B	B	A	T	H
P	E	N			S	U		A		T	O	E
E		T	O		T	E	A	C	H		N	R
N	O			W	I	S	D	O	M		I	
T	E		S	H	E		D			A	S	S
E		T	H	E	S	E		H		A	H	I
R	A		I	N		T	H	E		L	E	S
		I	N	C	H		C	A	B		D	T
O	F			E	E	L		L	E	A		E
W	O	R	K		R	A	G		A	G	A	R
N		S	Y	N	A	G	O	G	U	E		S

No. 27

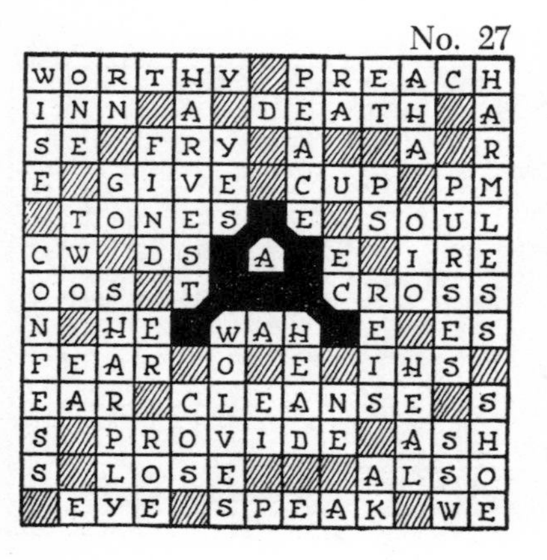

W	O	R	T	H	Y		P	R	E	A	C	H
I	N	N		A		D	E	A	T	H		A
S	E		F	R	Y		A			A		R
E		G	I	V	E		C	U	P		P	M
	T	O	N	E	S		E		S	O	U	L
C	W		D	S		A		E		I	R	E
O	O	S		T				C	R	O	S	S
N		H	E		W	A	H		E		E	S
F	E	A	R		O		E		I	H	S	
E	A	R		C	L	E	A	N	S	E		S
S		P	R	O	V	I	D	E		A	S	H
S		L	O	S	E				A	L	S	O
	E	Y	E		S	P	E	A	K		W	E

No. 28

H	E	A	D	S		M	I		B	U	Y	
U	R		O	P		O	V	E	R		E	A
N		T	W	E	L	V	E		A	W	A	Y
D		A	N	N	I	E		S	K	A	R	E
R				T		D	O		E	D		S
E					T			S			E	
D	R				W			E			A	
S	E	T			O			E			T	
			A	T		I	T		R	O		S
F	I	S	H	E	S		R	I	O		S	E
I	S	A	I	A	H		A		U		E	N
V	I	M		C	O	M	M	A	N	D	E	D
E	S		S	H	E	E	P		D	E	N	

No. 29

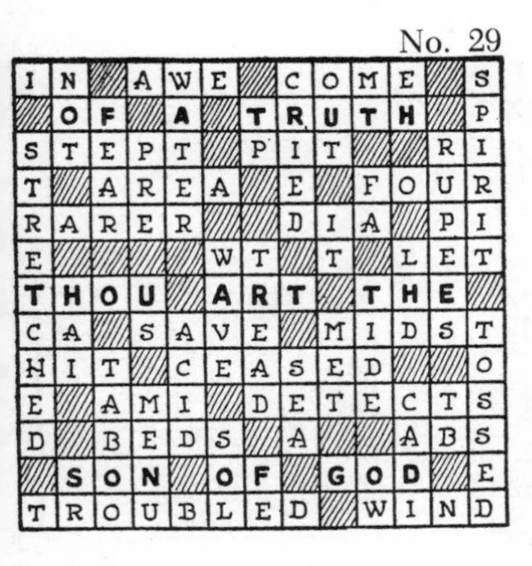

No. 30

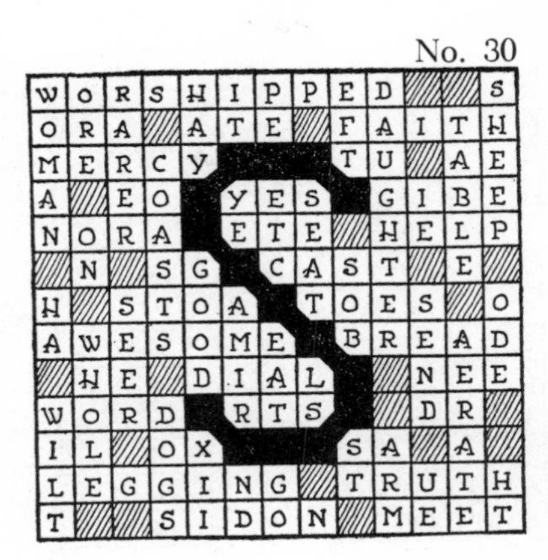

No. 31

A	N	D		U	P	O	N		T	H	I	S
R	O	C	K		O	N	O		L	E	N	A
	W			K	I	E		H		A		Y
I		W	I	L	L		B	U	I	L	D	
M	Y		C	H	U	R	C	H			R	P
		Y	E			E	L		A	S	E	A
A	N	D		T	H	E		G	A	T	E	S
O	F		H	E	L	L		U		R		S
		P	O				E	L	I	A	S	
S	E	L		S	H	A	L	L		N	O	T
P	R	E	V	A	I	L		I	N	G		H
A	G	A	I	N			O	E		E	L	A
N	S		A	G	A	I	N	S	T		I	T

No. 32

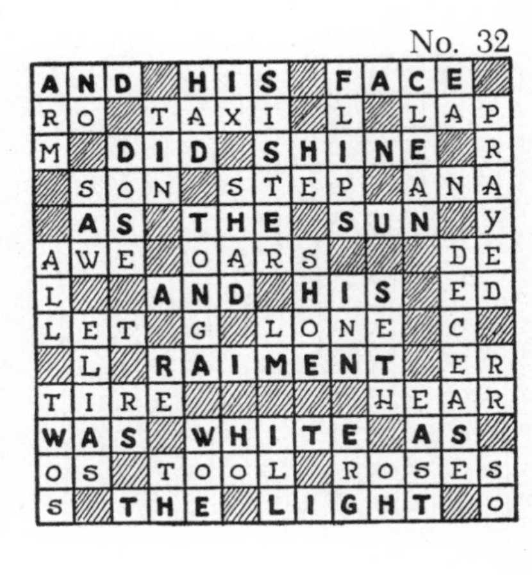

No. 33

C	O	D	A	S		M	E		W	H	A	T
	F	**O**	**R**		**H**	**E**		**T**	**H**	**A**	**T**	
G	T		M	E	E	T			I	T		C
R		**I**	**S**		**L**	**E**	**A**	**S**	**T**		A	H
E	M	S		O	D		G	O	E	S		I
A	**M**	**O**	**N**	**G**		**Y**	**O**	**U**		**A**	**L**	**L**
T	E		A		H	E	R		S	T	A	D
E		**T**	**H**	**E**		**S**	**A**	**M**	**E**		S	R
S	O			R	G			O	V	A	T	E
T		**S**	**H**	**A**	**L**	**L**		**B**	**E**			N
	O	E	S		A		W		R	A	N	
A	N	N		**G**	**R**	**E**	**A**	**T**		M	O	P
S	E	T		R	E	A	S	O	N	I	N	G

No. 34

O	W	E	S	T		D	E	B	T		L	P
N	O	S	E		P	E	N	C	E		O	R
E	R		V							P	S	I
	S	E	E		T	R	E	S	P	A	S	S
W	H	E	N		E	S	T	R	A	Y		O
O	I	L			N	E		I	T		M	N
A	P		F						I	S	O	
D	P		O		T	O		F	E	E	T	
	E	A	R		W	E		E	N	V	O	Y
	D	O	G		O		U	L	C	E	R	S
A			A			I		L	E	N	S	
S	E	R	V	A	N	T		O		T		I
A	G	R	E	E		S	A	W		Y	O	U

No. 35

M		**T**	**H**	**E**		**N**	**I**	**G**	**H**	**T**		A
A	P	H	I	S				S	E	E		N
N	R		S		C	E	E		A	A		O
I	A	M		D	A	Y		E	R	R		I
F	I		**C**	**O**	**M**	**E**	**T**	**H**				N
E	S	E		R	E	S	T		H	A	S	T
S	E	N	T					A	E	R	I	E
T			E	A	R	S		B	L	I	N	D
	W	**H**	**E**	**N**		**N**	**O**		**M**	**A**	**N**	
S	A	T		T	O		F	A		S	E	C
P	S		A		N	J		S	A		D	L
A	H		G	R	E	E	D		S	T		A
T		**C**	**A**	**N**		**W**	**O**	**R**	**K**		A	Y

No. 36

		I		**A**	**M**		**T**	**H**	**E**		S	O
	N		I	S		S	A	I		I	T	
G	**O**	**O**	**D**		**S**	**H**	**E**	**P**	**H**	**E**	**R**	**D**
O	T			W	C	A		P	A		A	O
E		**T**	**H**	**E**		**G**	**O**	**O**	**D**		N	O
T	H	E	I	R	S		W		A		G	R
H		**S**	**H**	**E**	**P**	**H**	**E**	**R**	**D**		E	
	S	T					S	A		A	R	T
T	E		**G**	**I**	**V**	**E**	**T**	**H**		D		H
H	E	A	R		I	R			L	O	V	E
I		**H**	**I**	**S**		**L**	**I**	**F**	**E**		I	M
E	V	E	N	E	D		F	O	A	M	S	
F	**O**	**R**		**T**	**H**	**E**		**S**	**H**	**E**	**E**	**P**

No. 37

T	W	O		D	E	S	P	I	S	E	T	H
A	O		O	U	T		R		E	G	R	E
M	E	A	N	S		D	O	W	N		E	A
E		R	E	T	U	R	N	E	D		A	R
					R	O	E			O	D	E
R		B	E		N	P		S	H			T
E	S		Y		S			E	I		R	H
P	E	R	E			P		E	D		E	
E	T	E	S		S	O	N			I	C	I
N		M		O		W	R	I	T	T	E	N
T	H	A	N	K		E		S	O		I	N
E	L	I			E	R	I		S	A	V	E
D		N	I	G	H		F	A	T	H	E	R

No. 38

	M	A	S	T	E	R		W	H	A	T	
P	A	S	S	E	D		L	I		R	A	N
I	R	K		N		P	E	N	C	E		E
N	E		C		G	A	V	E			S	I
	S	H	A	L	L		I		D	O		G
L		P	R	I	E	S	T		I		R	H
A	N		E		N	I	E	C	E		A	B
W		C		V		G		O			G	O
	T	O		I	N	H	E	R	I	T		U
S	A	M	A	R	I	T	A	N		E	R	R
I	C	E		G			S	U			A	
D	I		R	I	G	H	T		M	O	R	E
E	T	E	R	N	A	L		L	I	F	E	

No. 39

A	N	D		W	H	O	S	O	E	V	E	R
S	O		C	A	L	L	E	T	H		R	
K		C	A	R			E			O	I	L
	L	I	V	E	T	H		A	N	D		A
G	I	V	E		E	E	L		E	E		Z
L	P			A		R	O	D	S		P	A
O		B	E	L	I	E	V	E	T	H		R
R	O	O	T	S			E	A			M	U
Y		R	E		M	A	R	T	H	A		S
	I	N		M	E		S	H	A	L	L	
A	R		E	A	T	S			L	A	I	D
M	A	R	Y		R	I	S	E		T	E	A
I		N	E	V	E	R		D	I	E		Y

No. 40

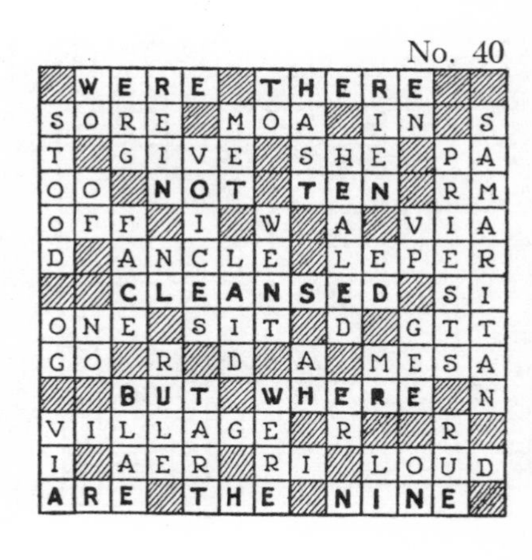

	W	E	R	E		T	H	E	R	E		
S	O	R	E		M	O	A		I	N		S
T		G	I	V	E		S	H	E		P	A
O	O		N	O	T		T	E	N		R	M
O	F	F		I		W		A		V	I	A
D		A	N	C	L	E		L	E	P	E	R
		C	L	E	A	N	S	E	D		S	I
O	N	E		S	I	T		D		G	T	T
G	O		R		D		A		M	E	S	A
		B	U	T		W	H	E	R	E		N
V	I	L	L	A	G	E		R			R	
I		A	E	R		R	I		L	O	U	D
A	R	E		T	H	E		N	I	N	E	

No. 41

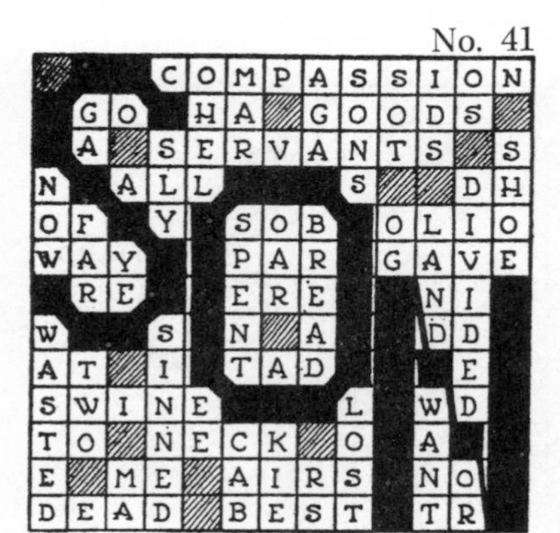

			C	O	M	P	A	S	S	I	O	N
	G	O		H	A		G	O	O	D	S	
	A		S	E	R	V	A	N	T	S		S
N		A	L	L				S			D	H
O	F		Y		S	O	B		O	L	I	O
W	A	Y			P	A	R		G	A	V	E
	R	E			E	R	E			N	I	
W			S		N		A			D	D	
A	T		I		T	A	D				E	
S	W	I	N	E				L		W	D	
T	O		N	E	C	K		O		A		
E		M	E		A	I	R	S		N	O	
D	E	A	D		B	E	S	T		T	R	

No. 42

C		A	N	D		C	O	M	E		L	P
O		W	E		L	A	N	E	S		O	O
M	O	A		G	A	L	E	A			V	S
M	A	Y	S		C	L		S	A	K	E	S
A	T		T	A	K	E		U	P		D	E
N	H		A	C	E	S		R	E			S
D		T	R	U	S	T		E	D	G	E	S
M	U			T	T		A			O		I
E		T	H	E		C	R	O	S	S		O
N	O	R	A		S	A		R	A	P	I	N
T	H	E	R	E		M	A		D	E	N	S
		A	D		S	E	L	L		L		
A	N	D		F	O	L	L	O	W		M	E

No. 43

S	A	L	V	A	T	I	O	N		W	E	D
Y	E	T		G	O			I	M	A	G	O
C	R		J	O	Y	F	U	L	L	Y		W
A	Y	E									A	N
M			P	R	E	S	S		A	S	P	
O	H		O	I	L	S		C	H	I	E	F
R	A		O	C	A		H	O		N		O
E	S		R	H		U		M	A	N		U
	T	O			A	P	S	E		E	A	R
H	E	R								R		F
A			S	A	W		R	A	W		S	O
L	I	T	T	L	E		A	R	E		E	L
F	A	L	S	E		E	N	T	E	R	E	D

No. 44

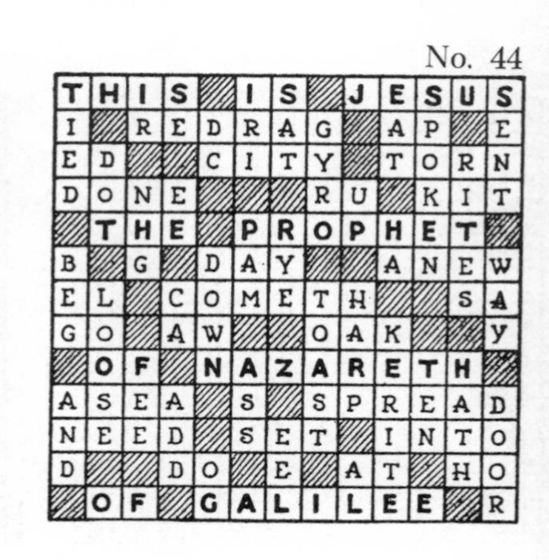

T	H	I	S		I	S		J	E	S	U	S
I		R	E	D	R	A	G		A	P		E
E	D			C	I	T	Y		T	O	R	N
D	O	N	E				R	U		K	I	T
	T	H	E		P	R	O	P	H	E	T	
B		G		D	A	Y			A	N	E	W
E	L		C	O	M	E	T	H			S	A
G	O		A	W			O	A	K			Y
	O	F		N	A	Z	A	R	E	T	H	
A	S	E	A		S		S	P	R	E	A	D
N	E	E	D		S	E	T		I	N	T	O
D			D	O		E		A	T		H	O
	O	F		G	A	L	I	L	E	E		R

No. 45

No. 46

No. 47

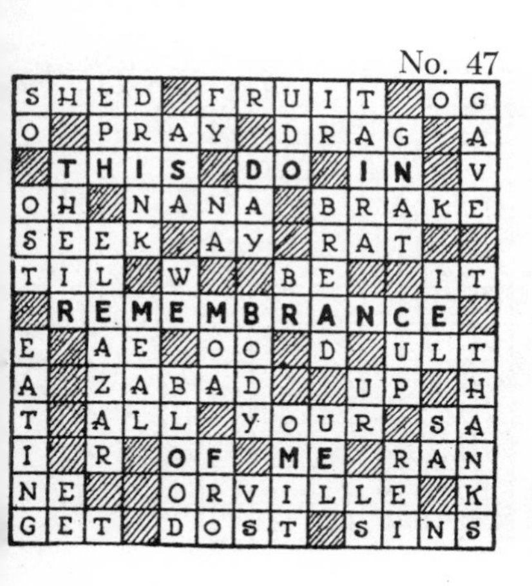

No. 48

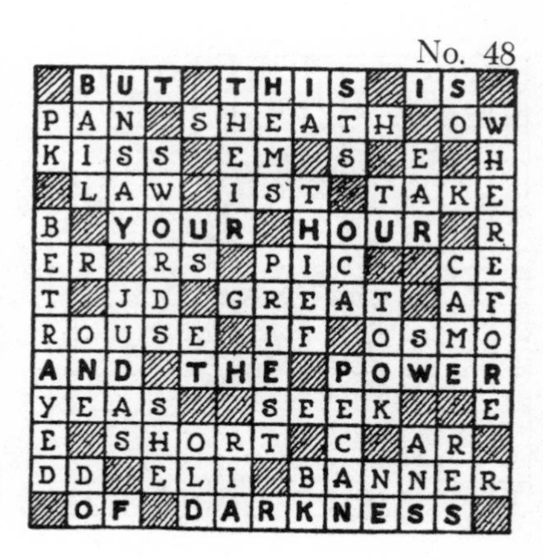

No. 49

I		**F**	**I**	**N**	**D**		O	T	H	E	R	S
	S		L	A	W		P	R	I	V	E	T
A	I	S		P	A		E	I		E	L	I
C	R	E	W		R	N		A		N	E	R
C		**N**	**O**		**F**	**A**	**U**	**L**	**T**		A	R
U		D	R	I	E	T	H		R	I	S	E
S	A		L		D	I	D		U		E	T
A	C	I	D	S		O	E		T	R		H
T	T				**I**	**N**		**T**	**H**	**I**	**S**	
I		D	A	L	E		K			F	O	B
O	N	O		E		F	I	G	H	T		O
N	O	N	E	S		O	N	E	S		I	R
	D	E	A	T	H		G	T		**M**	**A**	**N**

No. 50

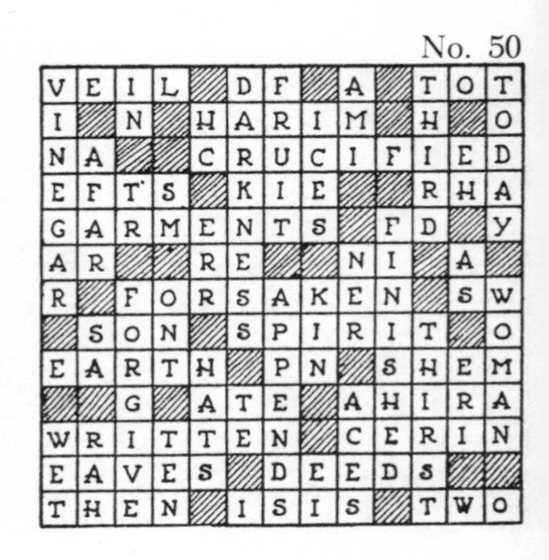

No. 51

S	T	O	N	E		G	A	R	M	E	N	T
E	O		E	R	I		L	I	E		O	R
P	L	A	C	E		R	I	S	E	N		E
U	D	O						E	T		A	M
L			M		W	A	Y			H		B
C	A	M	E		S	E	E		T	E	L	L
H	R							A		R	O	E
R	O	L	L		H		A	S	C	E	N	D
E	M	I	T		A	F		H	I		G	
	A	V			L	I	S		N	U		S
T		I		A	F	R	A	I	D		R	E
W	A	N	E	D		S	I	D	E		A	E
O		G	R	E	A	T			R	A	N	K

No. 52

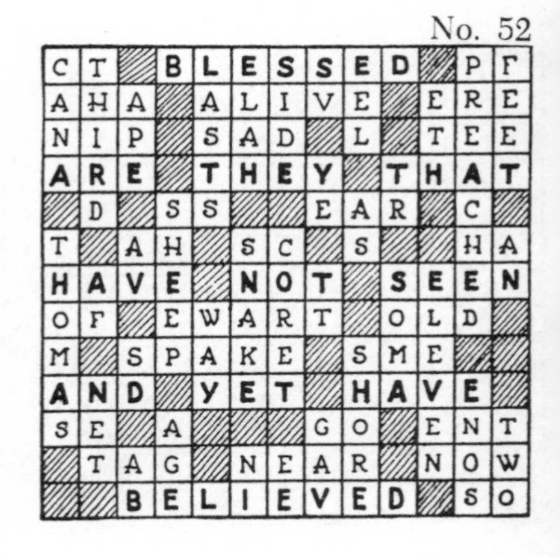